Let's Target™

Comprehension

6

TEACHERS AT WORK

Sadlier School

Comprehension

Teachers at work™ an imprint of Sadlier School, was created by teachers with teachers in mind to provide the right materials to support students with achieving academic success. Teachers all over the country contributed their ideas and expertise to bring together opportunities for students to practice essential skills and strategies with engaging print and online resources. Together they built a program that will support both teachers and students. We are excited to share these engaging print and online resources with you.

Sadlier School

Cover Series Design: Studio Montage, St. Louis, MO, United States of America

For additional online resources, go to sadlierconnect.com.

 is a trademark of William H. Sadlier, Inc.

William H. Sadlier, Inc.
9 Pine Street
New York, NY 10005-4700

Printed in Singapore.
ISBN: 978-1-4217-4726-2
1 2 3 4 5 6 7 8 9   19 18 17 16 15

PREFACE

Welcome to the *Let's Target*™ Series

Teachers at work™ is excited to introduce this new series to support students in mastering the Common Core State Standards.

The *Let's Target* series was developed by teachers. We understand students need to be engaged in their learning to succeed. With a simple, yet systematic approach, students learn skills and gain confidence to successfully meet the Common Core Standards.

"I got it!" That's what we want students to say when they focus on the lessons in the *Let's Target* series. As teachers, we know how hard it can be to find the right material to boost student achievement. With the *Let's Target* series, students complete the exercises in the book and then go online to reinforce what they have learned.

Want to flip it? Go ahead! Begin with the online resources to jumpstart the learning and then complement the activities with lessons from the book. Either way, students and teachers will be happy to get more opportunities to learn and practice essential skills.

Do you want to work independently or with a peer? *Let's Target* allows for all different kinds of learning strategies. Teachers will find more guidance about this in their Teacher's Guides.

Getting ready for Common Core Assessments? Since the beginning of the Common Core State Standards many have wondered how to prepare students for success. *Let's Target Comprehension* provides opportunities for students to read more complex text and apply comprehension strategies across different content-area topics.

***Let's Target Comprehension* for summer learning?** With *Let's Target Comprehension*, students will have a broad range of text themes and genres that will allow them to read widely and deeply and come back to school ready for success!

Hey Students! Demonstrate your independence by closely reading the range of text in this book and responding to the text-dependent questions at the end of each passage. Give yourself a push to be successful on the new Common Core assessments by mastering comprehension.

The components of the *Let's Target* series include:
- Student Editions with lots of opportunities for **"I got it!"** moments
- Teacher's Guides which support teachers with **CCSS connections** and problem solutions
- Online Resources give students and teachers the tools to **blend learning** and engage in learning in the classroom and at home

Teachers from around the country collaborated through **Teachers at work** ™, contributing ideas and expertise, to develop this series to prepare students for academic success. Please let us know if you have any ideas that will support students in reaching school success! Contact us at TeachersAtWork@Sadlier.com.

Teachers at work

CONTENTS

MCQ = Multiple Choice Questions
OE = Opened-Ended Questions

BASIC

INTERMEDIATE

CONTENTS

ADVANCED

NOTE:

Let's Target Comprehension is designed for students to practice and gain proficiency in answering the different types of comprehension questions found in the multiple-choice and open-ended formats.

The passages are analyzed and categorized into *Basic, Intermediate,* and *Advanced*.

The **Basic** level aims to increase student's expertise in making meaning.

In the **Intermediate** level, the passages encourage higher-level thinking and analytical levels of comprehension.

The **Advanced** level encourages students to think beyond the ideas presented in the passages, develop deep comprehension, and prepare students for high-level comprehension of complex texts.

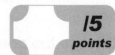

EXERCISE 1

/5 points

Read the passage carefully.

A wise man was traveling through a forest one night when he suddenly came face-to-face with a terrible giant. The giant told him that he was going to eliminate him. The wise man calmly said, "Very well, try if you may, but I can defeat you, for I am more powerful than you think."

5   "Nonsense!" said the giant. "You cannot defeat me because I am ten times larger than you."

"If you want a test of strength, take this stone and squeeze liquid out of it," said the wise man as he picked up a small piece of rock and handed it to the giant. The giant tried very hard but he could not.

10   "It is impossible; there is no water in this stone. Show me how," the giant demanded. In the darkness, the wise man took an egg out of his pocket, and squeezed the stone and the egg together, holding his hand over them. The giant was impressed when he saw liquid oozing out of the stone.

"I must think this over," the giant said. "Come to my cave and you can 15   spend the night there." The wise man accompanied him to a huge cave. The giant told him where to sleep and immediately, he fell asleep himself.

As soon as the giant was asleep, the wise man got up. He knew the giant would kill him in the middle of the night. Quietly, he arranged his bed to give the impression that he was still in it. After doing so, he hid himself at 20   a place some distance from the giant.

No sooner had he hidden himself then the giant woke up. He picked up a tree trunk with one hand and struck seven heavy blows on the dummy in the wise man's bed. Then, he lay down again and went to sleep. The wise man returned to his bed, lay down, and called out to the giant, "Oh giant! 25   This cave of yours is comfortable but I have been bitten seven times by a mosquito. You really should do something about it."

This shocked the giant so much that he dared not attempt a further attack. The giant immediately went down on his knees and begged the wise man for forgiveness.

Choose the correct answer and fill in the correct letter in parentheses.

1 The wise man showed the giant that he could _____.
  (a)   squeeze liquid out of a stone
  (b)   become ten times bigger than he
  (c)   break an egg with a stone
  (d)   perform magic tricks

2 The egg-and-stone trick proved that the wise man was _____.
  (a)   smarter   (c)   faster
  (b)   braver   (d)   stronger

3 Thinking that the wise man was in bed, the giant _____ .
  (a)   covered him with a blanket
  (b)   used a tree trunk to strike him
  (c)   provided him with a dummy
  (d)   helped to arrange his bed

4 The giant was greatly surprised when the wise man told him that
_____.

  (a)   his cave was comfortable   (c)   he had been bitten by a mosquito
  (b)   he hid at some distance   (d)   the dummy was not him

5 The wise man was able to defeat the giant through _____.
  (a)   flattery   (c)   strength
  (b)   obedience   (d)   trickery

Glossary

face-to-face (line 2): having a conversation or meeting with the person you are looking at
The human resource manager called me to arrange for a face-to-face interview next Monday.

eliminate (line 3): to kill someone so that he does not cause trouble to you
The king ordered the assassin to eliminate all those who stood in his way.

EXERCISE 2

/22 points

Read the passage carefully.

The social weaverbird is a close relative of the common house sparrow. Unlike the common sparrow which makes a small, untidy nest on a window ledge or on a tree branch, the weaverbird makes a huge apartment-like nest by tightly weaving together leaves, grass, twigs and so on.

5   The social weaverbirds live on the dry, flat lands of southern Africa. They live in large colonies of thirty or more pairs of birds. The birds work together in building their huge nests. However, two weaverbirds have their own "apartment" or nesting chamber.

The huge nests are often located among the thorny branches of an acacia
10   tree. The nests may be three or four yards long and two to three yards wide. Some nests have been known to house more than one hundred weaverbird families.

There are many other kinds of weaverbirds that build unusual nests. While none are as large as the nests of the social weaverbirds, some are
15   quite interesting. Some kinds of tropical weaverbirds build nests that look like wine flasks. The nests hang down from tree branches or tall grass. The male weaverbirds usually do most of the nest building.

Most kinds of weaverbirds are excellent nest-builders but there are a few exceptions. Widowbirds, members of the weaverbird family, do not build
20   nests at all. Instead, the females lay their eggs in the nests of other birds. The host birds do not seem to be able to spot the difference. They hatch the widowbirds' eggs and raise the young.

Answer the following questions in complete sentences citing evidence from the text.

1 How is the social weaverbird different from the sparrow?

_____

_____

2 What do weaverbirds need to build their nests?

_____

_____

3 How many weaverbirds are there in a regular flock?

_____

_____

4 How many weaverbirds live in a single nesting chamber?

_____

_____

5 Why are weaverbirds called social birds?

_____

_____

6 What is so unusual about some of the weaverbirds' nests?

_____

_____

7 Why are the nests of some tropical weaverbirds unusual?

_____

_____

8 Which weaverbirds do not build nests?

_____

_____

9 Where do the widowbirds lay their eggs?

_____

_____

10 Who looks after the widowbirds' eggs?

_____

_____

11 What is the main idea of the text? How does the author develop this idea? Use examples from the text to support your analysis.

_____

_____

Glossary

window ledge (lines 2-3): a shelf below the window and can be found on either side of a building

The little bird hopped along the window ledge outside my bedroom before it spread its wings and flew off.

weave (line 4): to make something by crossing threads or thin pieces under and over each other

The women had been weaving these straw baskets since morning.

colony (line 6): a group of animals or plants of the same kind living or growing together

The colony of seals swam in the clear Arctic water.

MCQ

BASIC

EXERCISE 3

/5
points

Read the passage carefully.

     The leopard is a small animal compared to the lion and the tiger but many people think that it is the most dangerous of the big cats. For its weight, the leopard is one of the strongest of the cats. It is an excellent climber and can run up a tree with astonishing speed. It can even climb a tree while carrying

5 a prey twice its own weight. It can leap up more than three yards in the air and jump down on its prey from a height of fifteen yards.

     The leopard's skin of greyish gold with dark spots or rings provides excellent camouflage among the branches of a tree. Although the leopard may be seen during the day, it is most active at night.

10   The leopard is particularly dangerous because it hunts near towns and villages for dogs. Leopards sometimes can turn into deadly human-eaters. They terrorize large areas for years. A leopard can easily carry a full-grown person off into the bushes or up a tree.

     The late hunter, Jim Corbett, wrote about a leopard that killed four

15 hundred people before he shot it in 1910. Corbett said that human-eating leopards are rare but very difficult to stop because they are smart and wary. Such leopards still appear from time to time in India and Africa. However, most leopards will not attack people unless provoked or wounded.

Choose the correct answer and fill in the correct letter in parentheses.

 Why do many people consider the leopard as the most dangerous?
(a)   It is smaller than a tiger.
(b)   It can leap high into the air.
(c)   It is one of the strongest of the cats.
(d)   It can jump down from a great height.

(2) How strong is the leopard?
   (a) It can run up a tree with great speed.
   (b) It can carry a prey twice its own weight.
   (c) It is an excellent climber.
   (d) It can leap very high up in the air.

(3) What advantage does the leopard's skin offer?
   (a) It frightens away all the other animals.
   (b) It keeps the leopard warm at night.
   (c) It makes the animal very beautiful.
   (d) It hides the leopard well among the trees.

(4) Leopards roam near towns and villages because _____.
   (a) they are attracted by the dogs
   (b) they want to be particularly dangerous
   (c) they like the meat of humans
   (d) they enjoy the company of humans

(5) Most leopards will attack humans when _____.
   (a) they are disturbed or injured
   (b) they terrorize large areas for years
   (c) they are fully grown
   (d) they are near extinction

Glossary

camouflage (line 8): the way the color or shape of an animal or plant helps it to blend in with its surroundings so that they cannot be easily seen by prey or predators
The fur of the Arctic fox changes to white during winter, so it is able to camouflage itself easily in the wintry landscape.

terrorize (line 12): to frighten people on purpose by threatening to harm them
The delinquent teenagers terrorized the villagers so much that an urgent meeting was held to discuss what to do with them.

wary (line 16): to be very careful because you do not trust something or someone
I am wary of people who call me and tell me that I have won a prize in a lucky draw that I do not even remember entering for.

DATE: .... NAME: ....

CLASS: ....

/22 points

Read the passage carefully.

Organic food is defined as food grown or produced naturally as far as possible. No pesticide, additive or genetically modified organism is used in its agriculture. Organic food must be free from preservatives, and if processed, would be kept to a minimum.

5   Grown or produced in its natural form, organic food is a source of natural nutrients. Organic food is also known to have a higher level of Vitamin C and cancer-fighting antioxidants compared to the food grown or produced by conventional methods. In addition, organic farming is environmentally friendly as artificial chemicals, pesticides and fertilizers are not used. Water

10   pollution, thus, is greatly reduced. As such, soil fertility is maintained. Many also claim that organic food is more palatable.

However, organic food takes a longer time to grow or produce compared to food produced conventionally. Much more attention and labor are also required in its production. The lower produce poses financial concerns to

15   the farmers. Because of the time and effort put in by the farmers, consumers will find that organic food tends to be more expensive.

Answer the following questions in complete sentences citing evidence from the text.

1 How different is organic food from food grown or produced in the conventional way?

_____

_____

Sadlier School

2 Why do people perceive organic food as healthy?

_____

_____

3 Explain "food grown or produced by conventional methods."

_____

_____

4 How does organic farming help to protect our environment?

_____

_____

5 Write down a word of your own to replace the word "palatable" in line 11.

_____

_____

6 List two disadvantages of producing organic food mentioned in the passage.

_____

_____

7 According to the passage, how different are organic food farmers from the other farmers?

_____

_____

(8) What are the financial concerns faced by organic food farmers?

_____

_____

(9) According to the passage, how does a consumer view organic food?

_____

_____

(10) Why do you think some people choose to consume organically grown food?

_____

_____

(11) What is the main idea of the text? How does the author develop this idea? Use examples from the text to support your analysis.

_____

_____

Glossary

genetically modified (line 2): living organisms such as animals humans or plants that have undergone changes in order to improve their quality

These huge red tomatoes have been genetically modified.

antioxidants (line 7): a substance in some types of food that helps to cleanse our body system

Blueberries are known to contain antioxidants.

conventional (line 8): the usual way of doing things

Growing crops without pesticides and fertilizers is not the conventional way plants are grown.

MCQ
BASIC

EXERCISE 5

/5
points

Read the passage carefully.

Mention the name Genghis Khan to most people and they think of one of history's most bloodthirsty conquerors. His Mongolian hordes massacred helpless prisoners and innocent civilians not only in millions but in tens of millions. His very name terrorized people for centuries afterwards.

5   However, he can be ranked along with Alexander and Napoleon as one of the greatest military geniuses. Temujin, who later became Genghis Khan, was the son of a minor Mongolian chieftain. He was orphaned at the age of eight and lived in constant danger from his father's enemies. In his teens, he began to build a power base amongst the scattered Mongolian
10   tribes. By means of wars, treachery and temporary alliances, he united the thirty tribes into one nation. He made his army into the most disciplined and well-trained one.

There were no foot soldiers in his army. Every man was a cavalryman and riding with a spare luggage horse. No army had ever been more mobile.
15   His men marched in great numbers many miles apart, destroying everything in their path, closing in to assist one another when necessary. They destroyed cities that resisted and murdered everyone in them but spared cities that surrendered.

Between 1211 and 1225, in a series of faultlessly brilliant campaigns,
20   Genghis Khan conquered a territory which covered China, northern India, Afghanistan, Iran and the whole of southern Russia. After his death, the Mongol Empire was extended until it stretched from Korea to Poland.

Choose the correct answer and fill in the correct letter in parentheses.

1 Why was Genghis Khan one of the most bloodthirsty conquerors?
   (a)   He massacred tens of millions of people.
   (b)   He instilled terror into people for centuries after.
   (c)   He was a great military genius.
   (d)   He lived in constant danger from his enemies.

2 Genghis Khan obtained his army from the _____.
   (a)   scattered Mongolian tribes   (c)   enemies of his father
   (b)   peoples of Asia   (d)   temporary alliances

3 Why was his army very mobile?
   (a)   His army was well-disciplined.
   (b)   They traveled in great numbers.
   (c)   Every soldier rode a horse.
   (d)   They assisted one another when necessary.

4 What did they do to cities that fought against them?
   (a)   They forgave them and spared their lives.
   (b)   They destroyed them killing everyone within.
   (c)   They made them part of their army.
   (d)   They set them ablaze and killed all the men.

5 What happened to his empire after his death?
   (a)   The empire was shared among his generals.
   (b)   The empire began to decline.
   (c)   The empire remained the same under one ruler.
   (d)   The empire grew bigger, covering more terrorities.

Glossary

bloodthirsty (line 2): to describe someone who enjoys killing and violence
The dictator was a bloodthirsty person who had no qualms in sending masses of people who disobeyed him to the execution ground.

massacre (line 2): to kill people in large numbers in a cruel way
The little boy broke down when he recalled how his entire family was massacred by the army of soldiers.

Sadlier School

Read the passage carefully.

A number of years ago, there was an old man who owned a small farm on the outskirts of a little town. He was very poor, for his farm was barren and useless. However, one fine day, the old man discovered gold in a stream that ran through his property. All his life he had been poverty-stricken but

5 the sudden fortune made him a very wealthy man. In fact, he became the richest man in town.

One of the first things the old man did was to buy himself a huge ostentatious car. He also bought himself a tall white hat, an expensive white suit and completed his outfit with a long, fat cigar. Every day, he would drive

10 through the dusty little town from one end of the street to the other. The old man would do so just to show off his new car. He wanted to see everyone and be seen by everyone. He was a friendly old man, so when driving through the town, he would turn both left and right to speak to everyone in sight. Interestingly enough, he never ran into anybody or over anybody. He never

15 did any physical harm or any damage to property. The reason was simple. Directly in front of that big beautiful car were two horses pulling it.

Local mechanics said that there was nothing wrong with the car engine but the foolish old man had never learned to drive. He did not even know that he had to insert the key and switch on the ignition. He did not know

20 that when the engine was switched on, the car could be more powerful than the two horses.

Answer the following questions in complete sentences citing evidence from the text.

1. What was the old man's occupation?

_____

_____

2. The farm was on the "outskirts" of the town (line 2). What does this mean?

_____

_____

3. Why was the old man "poverty-stricken" (line 4)?

_____

_____

4. Why did the gold belong to the old man?

_____

_____

5. Why did the old man buy a huge, expensive car?

_____

_____

6. Write down the sentence that suggests that the old man was boastful.

_____

_____

7 What is the difference between to run "into anybody" and "over anybody" (line 14)?

_____

_____

8 Why did the old man use horses to pull his car?

_____

_____

9 Which sentence shows that the strength of the car is greater than that of the horses?

_____

_____

10 What did the old man do that was most foolish?

_____

_____

11 What is the main idea of the text? How does the author develop this idea? Use examples from the text to support your analysis.

_____

_____

Glossary

outskirts (line 2): the part or area of a town or city that is the furthest from the center
The hotel that we were staying at was located on the outskirts of Frankfurt near the Polish border.

poverty-stricken (line 4): extremely poor
In a study done in the United States, it was found that poverty-stricken urban areas had a high percentage of people with the incurable AIDs virus.

ostentatious (line 8): an expensive item used to impress people
Her ostentatious lifestyle is often reported in the tabloids.

ignition (line 19): the electrical part of a vehicle's engine that causes the fuel to burn so that the engine can start
My mother turned on the ignition and got ready to drive out of the garage.

EXERCISE 7

/5 points

Read the passage carefully.

A wolf had a fox with him and made him do all the dirty work. The fox would have escaped but the wolf was stronger and faster than he was, so he had to do as he was told. One day, as they went through the forest, the wolf told the fox to bring him something good to eat or he would eat him
5 instead.

"I know a farm," replied the fox, "where there are many little lambs. I will bring you one if you like." This suited the wolf very well, so the fox went and stole a lamb and brought it back to the wolf. After the meal, the wolf thought he would follow suit and go and steal another lamb for himself.
10 However, he was so clumsy in his attempt that the lambs saw him and started to bleat. The farm people came running out with clubs. They beat the wolf so mercilessly that he fled, limping and groaning.

"You have made a fool of me," complained the wolf when he saw the fox. "When I tried to steal another lamb, all the farm people rushed out and
15 nearly beat me to death!"

The next day, the wolf asked the fox to bring him something to eat or he would eat him instead.

"I know a man," replied the fox, "who keeps a great amount of salted meat in his cellar. Let's go and eat it."

20 "Fine," said the wolf. "But I want you to help me if we are attacked." The fox agreed and showed him the way to the cellar. There was plenty of meat there and the wolf made a huge meal of it. The fox ate a little but he kept running back to the hole by which they had entered, to see if his body was still slim enough to slip through it. The wolf kept on eating until all the
25 salted meat was almost gone. Meanwhile, the owner of the house, who had been disturbed by all the noise, came to see what was happening. As soon as the fox caught sight of him, he was out in a flash but the wolf had eaten so much that he got stuck in the hole, and could move neither forward nor backward. The man seized a huge club and struck the wolf dead. The fox
30 trotted off into the forest, delighted to be rid of the old glutton.

Choose the correct answer and fill in the correct letter in parentheses.

1 Why was the fox willing to do all the dirty work?
  - (a) He was afraid of the wolf.
  - (c) He pitied the wolf.
  - (b) He was loyal to the wolf.
  - (d) He liked the wolf very much.

2 What caused the farm people to come running out with clubs?
  - (a) They heard the wolf.
  - (b) They heard their lambs bleating.
  - (c) The fox informed them.
  - (d) The wolf entered the house.

3 The fox ate only a little of the salted meat because _____.
  - (a) he wanted the wolf to have most of it so that he would be happy
  - (b) he had already eaten a lot earlier on and could not eat anymore
  - (c) he wanted to remain slim enough to slip through the hole
  - (d) he was busy keeping an eye out for the owner

4 The fox ran away the moment _____.
  - (a) he was disturbed by the noise
  - (c) there was a flash
  - (b) he saw the owner
  - (d) the man seized a huge club

5 The wolf got himself stuck in the hole _____.
  - (a) because he was a glutton
  - (b) because he was clumsy
  - (c) in order to save the fox
  - (d) so that he could block the owner's way

Glossary

follow suit (line 9): to act or behave in a similar fashion as someone who has just done so
Mr. Lee showed his son how he would cross the fast-moving river and expected him to follow suit.

club (line 11): a thick heavy stick used for hitting
The pictures depicted cavemen who held their clubs in their hands as they went about their daily lives.

glutton (line 30): someone who eats too much
The glutton ate all the food at the party.

EXERCISE 8

/22 points

Read the passage carefully.

Mother Teresa is well-known for her kind-heartedness and generosity throughout her daily life. She dedicated her life to helping the poor and the infirm, providing shelter for them and making sure that they were well taken care of.

5 She was a common sight at places of suffering such as Beirut and Chernobyl. Famine-racked places and earthquake zones were familiar with the caring face of Mother Teresa. Many people felt that she was like an angel in her white and blue sari. She provided care for those whom the rest of the world shunned. She always went the extra mile, choosing instead to take

10 the arduous route. Mother Teresa could have stayed away from the poor, giving instructions instead to those who could have helped her to carry out her work. She lived among the poor and the sick, eating the same food and sleeping under the same conditions as them.

Mother Teresa started her work with the poor by starting a school for

15 poor children. Children who would not have had an education otherwise were taken off the streets and given a chance to learn literacy. Later, Mother Teresa studied medicine and went into the homes of the sick to treat them.

When Mother Teresa started her homes, those who were turned away from other homes were taken in by Mother Teresa. She never turned away

20 any one who came knocking at her door. Mother Teresa was not afraid of catching the diseases that the sick had. Neither was she unwilling to help those who were suffering from terminal diseases.

With the large number of people needing help, Mother Teresa's charity grew and the number of homes set up by her increased over the years. A

25 network of homes was started and other nuns, like Mother Teresa, from the

Roman Catholic order volunteered to work with her to bring refuge to the poor and unwanted in the poorest parts of the world. Besides homes for the sick, there were also children's homes for the many children who had been abandoned by their parents or were victims of war. Food centers where the
30   poor could come for free food and places that were refuge for the insane and the aged were also part of the network.

Answer the following questions in complete sentences citing evidence from the text.

1   What types of people did Mother Teresa help?

_____

_____

2   Which word tells you that Mother Teresa was very committed to what she was doing?

_____

_____

3   From what two things did the places that Mother Teresa went to suffer?

_____

_____

4   How did Mother Teresa go the extra mile?

_____

_____

5   What type of people did Mother Teresa first help?

_____

_____

6 Why were some of the sick turned away from other homes?

_____

_____

7 Explain the meaning of 'terminal diseases.'

_____

_____

8 Why did Mother Teresa set up a network of homes?

_____

_____

9 What type of children did Mother Teresa help?

_____

_____

10 From where could the poor get their supply of free food?

_____

_____

11 What is the main idea of the text? How does the author develop this idea? Use examples from the text to support your analysis.

_____

_____

infirm (line 3): to be weak and ill for a long time
  The hospital is for those who are infirm.

shunned (line 9): to avoid something or someone on purpose
  We should not shun the poor in society.

arduous (line 10): something that requires a lot of effort and strength to do
  It was an arduous climb up the steep mountain.

network (line 25): groups of people that are connected to one another
  A network of food centers provide the poor with food.

 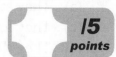

EXERCISE 9

/5 points

Read the passage carefully.

The wind suddenly rose, making a fearful howling sound. Lightning flashed across the darkened sky, followed by the deafening roar of thunder. An old woman stood outside her hut, looking anxiously towards the sea. Her eyes were searching the water for a boat as she prayed for the safe return of
5 her husband and son.

Meanwhile, two men were paddling as hard as they could, trying to make for the shore before nature unleashed its fury. The two fishermen had gone out to sea at the break of dawn in their small boat. Their catch had not been encouraging and they had decided to carry on until dusk to improve their
10 catch. However, they had not expected a storm which came so suddenly.

They had experienced the fury of nature before and had had many narrow escapes. However, they had a feeling that their flimsy wooden craft would not be able to withstand the onslaught this time. Hence, they paddled with every ounce of their strength, hoping to get back to dry land in time. Just
15 as it seemed they could make it, the storm arrived, full of sound and fury.

Heavy rain descended upon them. The sea heaved and tossed their boat like a cork. The wind blew them further out to sea as they clung on to their boat for dear life. They were now at the complete mercy of the storm. Under such conditions, there was nothing else they could do but pray for help.
20 No help came this time. All of a sudden, the boat was pushed sky-high by a mighty wave. When the wave subsided, the boat with its two occupants had disappeared.

Choose the correct answer and fill in the correct letter in parentheses.

1 Why did the two fishermen decide to fish until dusk?
  (a) They still had plenty of time.
  (b) They loved their work very much.
  (c) They did not catch enough fish.
  (d) They were greedy for more fish.

2 Which of these statements is correct?
  (a) The fishermen were not expecting a storm.
  (b) They carried on fishing in spite of the storm.
  (c) They knew that the storm would not last long.
  (d) They rowed out to sea to avoid the storm.

3 How did the fishermen feel about the storm?
  (a) They would have another narrow escape.
  (b) They would withstand it.
  (c) They would lose every ounce of strength.
  (d) They would not survive it.

4 The men prayed for help because _____.
  (a) the sea was heaving and tossing their boat
  (b) they were at the complete mercy of the storm
  (c) their boat was flimsy and made of wood
  (d) they were frightened and exhausted

5 What happened to the woman's husband and son?
  (a) They were washed ashore safely.
  (b) They were happily reunited with the woman.
  (c) The men lost their boat and their catch.
  (d) They were drowned in the storm.

Glossary

unleash (line 7): to suddenly let out a strong force that is usually destructive
  The manager's comments about the lack of cooperation among the staff in the department unleashed a wave of dissatisfaction.

flimsy (line 12): something that is not well-made or strong and can break easily
  He made such a flimsy airplane that it fell apart while in midair.

onslaught (line 13): a powerful attack
  The country suffered huge losses during the onslaught in World War Two.

EXERCISE 10

/22
points

Read the passage carefully.

The Olympic Games were an important event in ancient Greece. Now nearly ten thousand athletes from over one hundred countries take part in the dozens of events held once in every four years. These Games are open to athletes of every nation. They compete for the love of sports and not for
5   money.

The first modern Olympic Games were held in the Greek capital, Athens, in 1896. Fewer than three hundred athletes from just twelve countries took part in them. The main attraction of these games was the "marathon". This race was so named to honor a Greek runner who, centuries ago, ran
10   twenty-six miles from the battlefield at Marathon to Athens with news of a great victory.

In the first few Olympics, America was the most successful nation in winning the gold medals but soon the Europeans gained more successes. Perhaps, the most remarkable progress was made by Finland, a tiny country
15   of long, frozen winters. The long-distance runners of Finland were supreme for two decades. At Helsinki in 1952, the Russians competed in the Games for the first time. They put up a strong challenge for the American participants. In the last thirty years, African athletes as well as the Chinese athletes have become strong competitors in the Games. The 2004 Olympic Games was held
20   in Athens, where they originated from.

For many years, women were excluded from the Olympic competition. However, despite great opposition, they were finally admitted to the 1924 Games. They are achieving standards comparable to those of the men. However, it is unlikely that they will ever compete on equal terms with the
25   physically stronger men.

Answer the following questions in complete sentences citing evidence from the text.

(1) How many nations are involved in the present Olympic Games?

_____

_____

(2) In which country were the first modern Olympic Games held?

_____

_____

(3) What was the most important event in the first modern Olympic Games?

_____

_____

(4) How did the marathon get its name?

_____

_____

(5) Which country was the first to dominate the Olympic?

_____

_____

(6) In which Games did Russia make her first appearance?

_____

_____

7 When were female participants allowed to compete in the Games?

_____

_____

8 Why are women unlikely to compete with the men?

_____

_____

9 If the Olympic Games were held in 2002, what was the year the next Olympics Games was held?

_____

_____

10 Write down the phrase that tells us that woman athletes are obtaining results as good as men's.

_____

_____

11 What is the main idea of the text? How does the author develop this idea? Use examples from the text to support your analysis.

_____

_____

supreme (line 15): highest in position or rank
Zeus is the supreme god and ruler of Olympus.

exclude (line 21): to intentionally not include somebody or something
The children excluded him from the birthday party because they did not like his haughtiness.

opposition (line 22): an act which you strongly disagree with or protest against somebody or something
Despite opposition from his relatives and family, Fred insisted on selling his shares in the company.

EXERCISE 11

/5 points

Read the passage carefully.

Erwin Rommel made his name as a brilliant commander in the North African desert. Unlike most modern commanders, he always led from the front. Time and again, his rapid attacks from unexpected directions outwitted the British army. However, at last, he had to retreat from the vast forces
5　which the British piled up against him.

To his men, he was an adored hero. To the British, he was a chivalrous and humane enemy. When the German dictator, Hitler, ordered that all captured commandos should be instantly killed, Rommel refused to obey; he burned the paper giving the order. He even told Hitler that he should
10　punish his own men instead, for they had tortured and killed many innocent civilians.

In July 1944, he was severely wounded when his car was machine-gunned by a British fighter plane. Three days later, a number of German officers attempted to kill Hitler so that they could bring the war to an end.
15　The plot failed and many of the plotters were executed by Hitler's men. Hitler discovered that Rommel had given the plotters some encouragement.

One day, in October 1944, two men arrived at Field Marshal Rommel's home and informed him that he was sentenced to death because of the part he had played in the attempt on Hitler's life. However, because he was a
20　popular hero in the German army, he would have a choice. If he took poison, it would be announced that he had died from his wounds and he would be given a State funeral. If he refused, he would be publicly disgraced, tortured and executed together with his wife, son and personal staff. Rommel chose poison and died a German soldier admired even by his enemies.

Choose the correct answer and fill in the correct letter in parentheses.

1 Why was Rommel forced to retreat?
   (a)   The British had brilliant commanders.
   (b)   He disobeyed an order from Hitler.
   (c)   His enemies knew all of his tactics.
   (d)   The British had large forces against him.

2 Which of these statements shows that Rommel was humane?
   (a)   He was adored by his men.
   (b)   He dared to offend Hitler.
   (c)   He refused to kill captured commandos.
   (d)   He encouraged the attempt on Hitler's life.

3 What would happen if Hitler was killed?
   (a)   Rommel would be the new dictator.
   (b)   Most of the German officers would be executed.
   (c)   The British would invade Germany.
   (d)   The war would come to an end.

4 If Rommel chose the poison, he would _____.
   (a)   be publicly disgraced
   (b)   be buried as a war hero
   (c)   be tortured and executed
   (d)   die a natural death

5 What other reason did Rommel have for taking the poison?
   (a)   He hoped to protect the German army.
   (b)   He wanted to die without any pain.
   (c)   He hoped to please the dictator.
   (d)   He wanted to save his family.

Glossary

outwit (line 3): to be at an advantage over someone because of the use of trickery or clever plans
In a famous Aesop fable, the fox outwitted the crow by praising its beautiful voice so that the cheese it had in its beak would drop when it opened its mouth to sing.

chivalrous (line 6): refers to a man who is polite, kind, generous and honorable especially towards women
Many women were in love with Jim because they liked his chivalrous nature.

EXERCISE 12

/22 points

Read the passage carefully.

When I arrived at Atlanta Airport, I learned that the flight from Cairo,
on which my brother was traveling, had been delayed in Paris with engine
trouble and was expected to arrive about an hour late. Normally, I could
pass the time quite happily, watching the planes land and take off but that
5   evening I had a splitting headache. I thought that the noise of the engines
might make it worse. I decided; therefore, to walk around to pass the
time.

First of all, I went back to the spot where I had parked my car to make
sure that all the doors were locked. The walk in the fresh air did me good,
10   for I felt slightly better as I entered the main airport building again. I made
my way to the restaurant where I ordered a cup of coffee. Some people were
obviously anxious about the time, and kept glancing at their watches; others
checked to see that they had their tickets, passports and money. When there
was a group of people, it was obvious to me which one was about to leave.
15   He was the center of everyone's attention and looked either very happy or
sad at the thought of departure. There was one woman who burst into tears
as she bade farewell to the relatives and friends who had come to see her off.

When I had finished my coffee, I went to the bookshop where I purchased
two magazines about travel. Then I made myself comfortable in a large
20   armchair in one of the waiting lobbies. I hardly had time to open one of my
magazines when someone placed his hand on my shoulder. It was an old
friend who was just about to leave on a business trip to Europe. Since we had
not seen each other for a long time, we sat down to chat — until the arrival
of my brother's flight was announced.

Answer the following questions in complete sentences citing evidence from the text.

1 Why was the writer at the airport?

_____

_____

2 Where did the writer's brother board his flight?

_____

_____

3 Why did the writer have to pass the time at the airport?

_____

_____

4 How would the writer have spent his time if he had not had a headache?

_____

_____

5 Why did the writer decide to walk around to pass time?

_____

_____

6 Why did the writer go back to his car?

_____

_____

7 What helped to relieve his headache?

_____

_____

8 Why do you think some people were "anxious about the time, and kept glancing at their watches" (line 12)?

_____

_____

9 How did the writer intend to pass his time after drinking his coffee?

_____

_____

10 How long did the writer have to wait before the arrival of his brother's flight was announced?

_____

_____

11 What is the main idea of the text? How does the author develop this idea? Use examples from the text to support your analysis.

_____

_____

Glossary

delay (line 2): to make someone or something late
I was slightly delayed for my meeting because of the flood at Orchard Road.

splitting headache (line 5): a very severe pain in the head
I am going to my room to rest because I have a splitting headache.

to pass the time (lines 6-7): to spend the time especially because you are bored or you are waiting for something or someone
I had decided to pass the time listening to some music at the music shop when my friend called me on my mobile phone to join her for lunch.

departure (line 16): the act of leaving a place
Joan gave each of us a final hug before her departure.

EXERCISE 13

/5
points

Read the passage carefully.

One day, a bird-keeper was feeding the king's favorite bird when it escaped from the cage and flew away. When the king learned of the incident, he was furious and immediately ordered that the bird-keeper be executed. As the news of the king's decision spread, people all over the kingdom were
5   distressed. They felt that their king was too harsh over a small matter. The king's minister realized this and was concerned about the king's reputation. He hurried to the palace and on entering the courtroom, bowed respectfully to the king, "I am sorry to hear that Your Majesty has lost a beautiful bird. You are indeed justified in sentencing the irresponsible bird-keeper to death,
10   for he has committed no less than three major offenses. Perhaps Your Majesty would permit me to point them out to the condemned man so that he can die knowing his mistakes."

The people in the room were astonished by the minister's words. How could anyone think that a person should lose his life just because he had
15   let a bird escape? The king, however, agreed to his minister's request. The bird-keeper was brought into the courtroom, chained and bound. His whole body trembled as he knelt before the king. The minister stepped forward and spoke in a clear, loud voice for everyone to hear, "Listen well. You have been careless in your duties and have allowed a valuable bird to escape. This
20   is your first offense. In addition, your negligence has angered your master, the king, causing him to have a man executed because of a little bird. This is your second offense."

"Finally, your execution will lead the people to believe that their king is cruel and ruthless since he values a pet far more than the life of a human
25   being. This is your third offense. Having committed these three major offenses, you deserve to die indeed."

The entire courtroom was silent. Everyone admired the minister's wit and courage. The minister turned towards the king and said, "Your Majesty, this man has now heard his crimes. The execution can proceed immediately."
30   After hearing the minister's speech, the king was ashamed. Then, in a calm

and sincere voice, he announced to the attentive court, "The prisoner will be freed. I am indeed fortunate to have my minister's wise counsel. Let everyone learn from his courage."

Choose the correct answer and fill in the correct letter in parentheses.

1 The king ordered the execution of the bird-keeper because _____.
  (a) the bird-keeper had angered his master
  (b) he had allowed the king's favorite bird to escape
  (c) he had committed three offenses
  (d) he did not inform the king of the incident

2 The people felt that their king was _____.
  (a) making a mountain out of a molehill
  (b) killing two birds with one stone
  (c) charging like a bull in a china shop
  (d) keeping the bird-keeper at arm's length

3 What was the king's minister concerned about?
  (a) The king would become harsh and cruel.
  (b) The bird-keeper would take his revenge on him.
  (c) The minister would lose his post to someone else.
  (d) The people would lose their respect for the king.

4 Why did the king release the bird-keeper in the end?
  (a) He pitied the prisoner.
  (b) He was afraid of the people.
  (c) He granted the minister's wish.
  (d) He realized his mistake.

5 Which of these statements is correct?
  (a) The minister pretended to agree with the king.
  (b) The people in the court were brave and just.
  (c) The king only wanted to frighten the bird-keeper.
  (d) The prisoner stood before the king without any fear.

Glossary

execute (line 3): to kill someone as a legal punishment
He was hauled out of the prison to be executed for treason.

condemned person (line 11): a person who is going to be punished by being killed
Louis knew he was a condemned man because he had played a part in the gruesome murder.

DATE: .... NAME: ....

CLASS: ....

EXERCISE 14

/22
points

Read the passage carefully.

Long ago, goods were manufactured by craftsmen who were very skilful. A craftsman was proud of each article he made. He would spend a long time in making it and took great pride in his work. Customers paid a high price for the craftsmanship. All the luxurious Persian carpets, the beautiful Chinese
5 pottery and the handmade lace of certain European countries were made in this way. But these articles were bought only by the rich. Poor people had to be satisfied with goods that were roughly and cheaply made.

When the population increased, there was a demand for goods of better quality. These goods had to be produced in factories and workshops where
10 hundreds of workers were employed. The invention of the steam engine helped manufacturers by giving them cheaper power to work their machines. Machines took the place of men and production was increased. People were able to buy articles of good quality at low prices. This is called mass production. Mass production means the manufacture of a large number of
15 identical articles by machinery. Cars, radios and cameras are examples of the many types of articles that are mass produced today.

A conveyor belt plays an important part in mass production. By means of a conveyor belt which moves continuously, articles are conveyed from one point to the next during the various stages in their manufacture. A lot
20 of time is saved in this way.

A visit to a factory is an interesting experience. Take, for example, a biscuit factory. The whole process of biscuit-making is done by machinery. First of all, the ingredients such as flour, sugar, fat and water are put into a mixing machine. The mixture comes out in the form of dough and is passed
25 on to a machine that presses it into molds. In these molds, the dough is given

the shape of biscuits. Then the biscuits are taken on the conveyor belt to the oven. As they move through the oven, they are slowly cooked. When they are cool, they are taken off the moving belt by workers and packed into boxes. The boxes are weighed, made airtight and wrapped. Then they are
30   ready to leave the factory.

Answer the following questions in complete sentences citing evidence from the text.

1 Why did customers pay a high price for articles made by craftsmen?

_____

_____

2 Name some well-known handicrafts mentioned in the passage.

_____

_____

3 Why were factories and workshops set up?

_____

_____

4 What was used to operate the machines?

_____

_____

5 What is meant by "machines took the place of men" (line 12)?

_____

_____

6 Write down the word from the passage that suggests the goods made are alike in every way.

_____

_____

7 What enabled the people to buy articles of good quality at low prices?

_____

_____

8 Why is the conveyor belt important in mass production?

_____

_____

9 How are the biscuits transported during the manufacturing process?

_____

_____

10 At which stage of the process are the biscuits actually touched by hand?

_____

_____

11 What is the main idea of the text? How does the author develop this idea? Use examples from the text to support your analysis.

_____

_____

Glossary

luxurious (line 4): extremely beautiful, expensive and comfortable
The Lee family bought a very luxurious villa to give to their son and daughter-in-law as a wedding gift.

convey (line 18): to transport something or somebody from one place to another
The goods are conveyed to the warehouse using the forklifts.

airtight (line 29): not allowing air to enter or get out
The half-opened packet of biscuits were placed in the airtight container.

DATE: .... NAME: ....

CLASS: ....

EXERCISE 15

/5 points

Read the passage carefully.

Tom was a healthy young man but he was a simpleton. When it was time for him to earn a living, his father could not get him any work. Finally, he became a herdsman, looking after his father's three buffaloes.

Tom found it difficult to distinguish one buffalo from another. Once he
5 had put his father's buffaloes in the field, he could not trace them among the buffaloes of other herdsmen. The other herdsmen knew this and they took advantage of it. They just lazed on the grass, laughing and joking, and whenever they saw a buffalo wandering out of the field, they shouted, "Tom, Tom, there goes your buffalo!" Tom, thinking every buffalo that wandered
10 out was his, spent the whole day chasing and catching the buffaloes. When evening came, he had to wait until the other herdsmen had taken away all their buffaloes before he could leave with his buffaloes. As a result, he arrived home late. This happened for many days until his anxious father found out the trick played on his son.

15 So the next day the father tied some leaves on the horns of his three buffaloes and said, "Now, my son, look at the buffaloes carefully and remember that only a buffalo which has leaves round its horns is your responsibility. Do not tire yourself by herding all the buffaloes in the field."

That morning, whenever the other herdsmen shouted, "Hey, Tom, there
20 goes your animal," Tom glanced at the buffalo's horns, and if he saw no leaves on its horns, he just sat down and took no further notice. However, by afternoon, Tom's secret had been discovered by his companions. They at once tied leaves onto the horns of their buffaloes, too. As a result, poor Tom again spent the entire afternoon chasing all the stray buffaloes. He arrived
25 home late again. His anxious father had been waiting for him at the gate of his farm. Tom complained, "Father, all was well in the morning but by afternoon, leaves have grown on the horns of the other buffaloes too."

Choose the correct answer and fill in the correct letter in parentheses.

1 Tom became a herdsman because _____.
- (a) it was his favorite job
- (b) he loved all sorts of animals
- (c) he was good at this type of work
- (d) there was no other job for him

2 The other herdsmen took advantage of Tom by _____.
- (a) lazing on the grass
- (b) laughing and joking with him
- (c) making him run after their own buffaloes
- (d) tricking him into giving them buffaloes

3 Why did Tom usually go home late?
- (a) He had to wait for the rest to collect their buffaloes.
- (b) He was tired after wandering all over the field.
- (c) He had to chase and catch his buffaloes first.
- (d) He needed more time to trace his buffaloes.

4 Why did Tom's father tie the leaves on the horns?
- (a) The buffaloes would be well hidden in the field.
- (b) The other herdsmen would not recognize Tom's buffaloes.
- (c) Tom would be able to distinguish his own buffaloes.
- (d) The buffaloes would not stray again.

5 Which of these statements is correct?
- (a) Tom knew the others used leaves to trick him.
- (b) Tom thought leaves were growing on the horns.
- (c) Tom did not believe that horns could bear leaves.
- (d) Tom felt that only his buffaloes could grow leaves.

Glossary

simpleton (line 1): refers to a person who is not very intelligent and can be easily tricked by others
Mrs. Frank was worried that her son, Tim, who was a simpleton, would be bullied by the neighbor's children when she went out to work.

distinguish (line 4): to recognize the difference between two things or people
Little Joshua was asked to distinguish between the mango and the papaya.

DATE: .... NAME: ....

CLASS: ....

EXERCISE 16

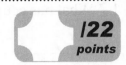

/22 points

Read the passage carefully.

Acupuncture is a traditional Chinese method for curing illnesses. However, it can also be used for aesthetic purposes. It can be used to make people beautiful.

Acupuncture has become an alternative to the knife and syringe.
5   Wrinkles are removed and pimples can disappear. This is simply done with a dozen microscopic needles that are inserted into the face. Those who have undergone the procedure say that despite the way it looks, it is completely painless. There is neither the use of anaesthetic nor a tedious recovery process. Patients only need to turn up for regular treatments at an acupuncturist clinic
10 for between one and three months.

Today, this method is gaining recognition beyond China. There is overwhelming interest in this method in America. The results are comparable to other methods but this method is also suitable for the man on the street and not just those who are affluent.

15 The greatest advantage of facial acupuncture is that it is a holistic method that aims to discover if the person's entire body is working properly. After a thorough examination of the patient, the acupuncturist can identify the root cause of the facial problem. Sometimes, wrinkles are caused by a problematic liver and that is where the needles would be targeted. The treatment will
20 therefore benefit a person's overall health.

Perhaps, one day, this method will be more widely used than cosmetic surgery.

Sadlier School

Answer the following questions in complete sentences citing evidence from the text.

1) What has acupuncture always been used for?

_____

_____

2) What method would make use of "the knife" (line 4)?

_____

_____

3) Describe how acupuncture to the face is done.

_____

_____

4) Why is anaesthetic not needed during an acupuncture treatment?

_____

_____

5) What is the after-effect of other treatments that are used to treat the face?

_____

_____

6) Where was acupuncture originally from?

_____

_____

7. Which phrase gives you an idea that acupuncture is not expensive?

_____

_____

8. What is a holistic treatment method?

_____

_____

9. Which part of a person's body does an acupuncturist insert the needles?

_____

_____

10. How do you think a person who has undergone facial acupuncture will feel after the treatment?

_____

_____

11. What is the main idea of the text? How does the author develop this idea? Use examples from the text to support your analysis.

_____

_____

Glossary

aesthetic (line 2): related to art and beauty
The fountain in the middle of the neighborhood is for aesthetic purposes.

microscopic (line 6): very small
These microscopic creatures can only be seen under a microscope.

tedious (line 8): something that is boring and seems to last for a long time
Without the Internet, finding out information on a particular subject can be a tedious process.

beyond (line 11): outside a place
There are many smaller islands beyond Singapore.

overwhelming (line 12): large quantity
The new artist received such an overwhelming support from his fans that tears of joy rolled down his cheeks.

affluent (line 14): rich; wealthy
He comes from an affluent family so he does not understand the importance of saving.

cosmetic surgery (lines 21-22): an operation that you go through to enhance your looks
Janet went for cosmetic surgery last week because she felt that she did not look as good as before.

EXERCISE 17

/5
points

Read the passage carefully.

Steven Paul Jobs and Stephen Wozniak were the founders of Apple Computer. The company gained a reputation for being the one who popularized the use of the computer in homes.

5 Steven dropped out of college but he attended classes sporadically including one in calligraphy. It was in this class that his knowledge was widened, allowing him to develop the different types of fonts for the Apple Computer later on.

However, the Apple Computer would not have materialized without Stephen. He was enthralled by electronics when he was young. Stephen
10 grew up in a home that encouraged exploration. His father, who was also an inventor, inspired Stephen. He taught Stephen the importance of scientific knowledge and finding creative solutions to problems. Today, Stephen uses his father's books to educate his children. He tells them how inventions can enrich a person's life.

15 His early attempts at building the computer failed but he later became the first one to develop a computer that was fully assembled instead of just a circuit board. This led to further improvements to the personal computer including the Macintosh with the addition of colors and pictures.

Today, the Macintosh is a powerful tool for playing games and, producing
20 and enhancing videos and photographs.

Choose the correct answer and fill in the correct letter in parentheses.

1 The Apple Computer was well-known because it _____.
   (a) was the first computer that people bought for their own use
   (b) was founded by Steven Paul Jobs and Stephen Wozniak
   (c) produced photographs and videos
   (d) could be used to play games

② According to the passage, Steven Paul Jobs was probably a person who
_____.
    (a)   came from a humble background
    (b)   was lazy and did not like to study
    (c)   did not like to learn electronics
    (d)   applied what he learned in school to his work

③ How did Stephen's childhood help him to develop the Apple Computer?
    (a)   His father told him about the importance of computers.
    (b)   He was always experimenting with new things.
    (c)   He read books that told him how important inventions were.
    (d)   He wanted to be wealthier than his father.

④ According to the passage, why were inventions important?
    (a)   They allowed people to make use of their scientific knowledge.
    (b)   They helped to build computers.
    (c)   They resulted in the creation of useful things.
    (d)   They prevented problems from happening.

⑤ When the Macintosh was first built, in what way was it probably different from other computers?
    (a)   It came with a circuit board.   (c)   It could be used to play games.
    (b)   It was fully assembled.   (d)   It had colors and pictures.

Glossary

reputation (line 2): the way people think of someone because of his character or behavior
Miss Randall has the reputation of being a kind and understanding teacher.

sporadically (line 4): something that happens at irregular intervals
The bird put the worm on the ground and pecked at it sporadically.

materialize (line 8): actually happening
The hike to the country did not materialize as most of the hikers backed out at the last minute.

enthralled (line 9): to be very interested in something
David was so enthralled by the book that he was reading that he did not hear me call him.

DATE: .... NAME: ....

CLASS: ....

EXERCISE 18

/22 points

Read the passage carefully.

Hundreds of children are dying from starvation and diseases in countries like Somalia and Ethiopia. The streets are filled with hungry children. It is common to see them scavenge for food together with the rats and stray animals. However, some are too frail to even move. A child lying in an alleyway might

5   not be sleeping. Something more tragic might have happened to him.

It is hard for many of us to empathize with these children. Many children are born into each family. Poverty prevents the parents from feeding their brood of children. The more fortunate ones receive aid from international volunteer organizations. Some villages are too remote, making it impossible

10   to reach them by truck. Walking in with supplies is unthinkable. For those who receive aid, they are immunized against diseases and receive sufficient nutrition for their age. Most importantly, when they are ill, there are ample medical facilities to take care of them. The most heart-wrenching thing is when help comes too late. It is even more difficult for the volunteers, who

15   are surrounded by their modern equipment, than the family members to watch a young child die.

On the other hand, children growing up in wealthier countries are beset with other health problems. Indoor activities such as playing video games and watching movies have become more popular than traditional outdoor

20   sports. There has been a sudden rise in obesity among these children. Junk food that is oily and rich in fats make up a large proportion of their diet. High blood pressure, heart attack and diabetes often result when these children grow older.

Answer the following questions in complete sentences citing evidence from the text.

1 What are the two causes of death among children in poor countries?

_____

_____

2 What is the similarity between stray animals and poor children?

_____

_____

3 What is the tragic event that could have happened to the child in the alleyway?

_____

_____

4 Why are families in poor countries unable to feed their children?

_____

_____

5 What obstacles do volunteer organizations face when they travel to villages?

_____

_____

6 What services do volunteer organizations provide for the children in poor countries?

_____

_____

7 What does the word "heart-wrenching" (line 13) tell you about the way the writer feels about the children?

_____

_____

8 According to the passage, why do family members find it easier to accept the death of the child than volunteers?

_____

_____

9 What type of lifestyle do children in wealthier countries lead?

_____

_____

10 What problems are linked with being fat in the writer's point of view?

_____

_____

11 What is the main idea of the text? How does the author develop this idea? Use examples from the text to support your analysis.

_____

_____

scavenge (line 3): to search for food among rubbish
  Beggars scavenge the streets for food every night.

frail (line 4): unhealthy and weak
  My grandmother has become very frail ever since she suffered the heart attack.

empathize (line 6): to understand a person's problems and feelings because you
                have gone through the same experience
  It is hard for children to empathize with their parents regarding the
  difficulties that they face in earning a living.

ample (line 12): enough of something and with extra to spare
  The villagers were prepared for the drought so there was ample food for
  everyone in the village during that time.

beset (line 17): to have so many problems and difficulties that you cannot deal with
                them
  The country was beset with problems when it was attacked by a powerful enemy.

DATE: .... NAME: ....

CLASS: ....

EXERCISE 19

Read the passage carefully.

As I settled down to write a letter to my pen pal, my thoughts drifted to the few days that she had spent with me. I could not help smiling at the hilarious situation that had occurred because she was unable to communicate with the locals here.

5   Coming from a rural town in Mexico, Sharin was unaccustomed to the lifestyle in New York City. As I was in school in the daytime, Sharin was left to explore the city on her own. Armed with a map and a lot of coins for traveling on the bus and train, Sharin decided to travel from one end of New York City to another. In this way, she would be able to see more of the

10   city and its people. She did not mind as she was an independent person.

Thinking that the bus service worked exactly like the ones in her hometown, Sharin shouted for the driver to stop when she wanted to alight. Imagine the stunned expressions on the other passengers' faces and the look of disbelief on the bus driver's. Not only was she unable to alight, some

15   people started whispering and pointing at her. She was so humiliated that she immediately got off at the next stop and took the subway back to my house instead.

I burst into hysterical laughter when she related the incident to me. Consoling her, I promised to be her companion during the weekend. Sharin

20   spent the next few days in my apartment watching television until I was free to take her out. Consoling her, I promised to be her companion during the weekend. Sharin spent the next few days in my apartment watching television until I was free to take her out.

Sadlier School

Choose the correct answer and fill in the correct letter in parentheses.

1 The writer and her pen pal _____.
(a) met each other on one of the bus rides
(b) often experienced funny situations together
(c) seldom spoke to each other
(d) met each other for a few days

2 How did the writer feel about her pen friend's experience on the bus?
(a) She felt sorry for her.
(b) She was angry with her.
(c) She thought it was amusing.
(d) She felt embarrassed.

3 Which of the following shows that Sharin was "independent" (line 10) ?
(a) She made sure she had coins with her for her transportation.
(b) She asked the bus driver to let her alight.
(c) She moved around the city on her own.
(d) She was able to communicate with the locals.

4 The incident on the bus probably made Sharin realize that _____.
(a) she was not allowed to shout in public
(b) the buses could only stop at designated places
(c) she was not supposed to talk to the bus driver
(d) people liked to whisper things about her and point at her

5 Why did Sharin watch television in the writer's apartment instead of going out?
(a) She did not want anything embarrassing to happen to her again.
(b) She did not have anyone to talk to.
(c) She did not like to take buses from then on.
(d) She was afraid of losing her way around the country.

Glossary

unaccustomed (line 5): not used to
When I first arrived in New Zealand, I was unaccustomed to its weather and kept falling ill.

alight (line 12): to step out of a vehicle
When the bus reached her house, she alighted and walked home.

stunned (line 13): shocked or surprised by something that you cannot speak
I was stunned to learn that my parents were injured in an accident.

hysterical (line 18): to be so excited or angry that it is difficult to control yourself
The old lady was wailing hysterically when she found out that her granddaughter had been kidnapped.

DATE: .... NAME: ....

CLASS: ....

EXERCISE 20

/22
points

Read the passage carefully.

The construction of budget air terminals attests to the popularity of budget airlines among frequent travelers today. Like the budget airlines, the budget air terminal is almost devoid of the amenities that we take for granted today.

5　　To cater to travelers who are departing, the current air terminals are now equipped with cable television, wireless points for travelers to access the Internet on their laptops and numerous cafes. However, the budget air terminal does not have these luxuries. Travelers can watch television but without the cable network, or browse around at

10　a few shops to while away the time. Other than that, there is little that they can do there.

There are no frills, only the essentials, at the budget air terminal. The departure hall has fewer chairs than it can accommodate. When interviewed, airport personnel explained that travelers had to get on line to get the seats

15　on the airplanes. No passenger is given priority when it is time for boarding.

What is noteworthy is the absence of airbridges in the budget air terminal. Travelers take for granted that they can always walk in air-conditioned comfort from the waiting area to the airplane and vice versa. In fact, few travelers have seen the exterior of an airplane. However,

20　passengers taking budget airlines will have to walk on the tarmac to get to the airplane. Under the scorching sun and often with hand luggage, the walk can be quite tedious.

Despite these inconveniences, many travelers are still willing to use budget airlines. They would rather spend more buying souvenirs in foreign

25　countries than on their air tickets.

Answer the following questions in complete sentences citing evidence from the text.

1 What is the difference between budget airlines and other airlines?

_____

_____

2 Why did some airports construct a new budget air terminal?

_____

_____

3 What do the "luxuries" (line 8) refer to?

_____

_____

4 Why are there "no frills" (line 12) in the departure hall of the budget air terminal?

_____

_____

5 Why does the departure hall at the budget air terminal have only a few chairs?

_____

_____

6 What is an airbridge used for?

_____

_____

7 Which sentence tells you that the sides of an airbridge are probably not made of glass?

_____

_____

8 What problems might the absence of airbridges have for passengers?

_____

_____

9 Why is traveling by budget airlines important for some travelers?

_____

_____

10 Explain why the writer considers the absence of airbridges "noteworthy" (line 16).

_____

_____

11 What is the main idea of the text? How does the author develop this idea? Use examples from the text to support your analysis.

_____

_____

attest (line 1): to show proof of
The delicious but cheap food attests to the popularity of the restaurant for the past ten years.

priority (line 15): the thing that is more important than any other thing or person
Families with three or more children will be given priority when boarding the airplane.

noteworthy (line 16): something that stands out because it is interesting or important
One noteworthy function of the vacuum cleaner is that it can be used to clear choked water pipes.

tarmac (line 20): a material used to make roads that are found at the airport for airplanes to take off or land
A bus was waiting on the tarmac to take the passengers from the airplane to the airport.

tedious (line 22): something that takes a long time to do
I hated playing the piano and I found it very tedious whenever I had to practice.

MCQ
INTERMEDIATE

EXERCISE 21

/5
points

Read the passage carefully.

About 13,000 years ago, at the end of the last ice age, a group of people known as the Paleoindians entered what was then called the New World. The place they inhabited was the American continent. Evidence has shown that the Paleoindians or the Clovis people were the ancestors of both North
5   and South America.

The Clovis were skilled hunters. Archaeologists have uncovered pointed tools that were perhaps attached to spears or lances to kill animals. They were made of lightweight material. These tools were portable yet effective and this allowed the Clovis to travel far distances to hunt the animals. The
10 Clovis were especially competent at hunting down huge animals. Today, Clovis weapons have been found alongside the skeletal remains of ice-age mammoths and mastodons. Meat from just one large animal could provide sustenance for the nomadic band of Clovis for a week. In winter, the meat was dried so that it could be preserved. The hides, bones and tusks of the
15 animals they killed were used to make some daily household possessions and tools.

Recent discoveries have shown that Clovis culture was not restricted to the huge animals that roamed the areas. The Clovis people were botanists as well who knew how to make use of plants for food and to make equipment
20 out of them. Besides turning to plants to cure ailments, it is believed that plant fiber was used to make items like baskets, nets and even clothes.

Choose the correct answer and fill in the correct letter in parentheses.

1   From the passage, we know that the Paleoindians _____.
   (a)   migrated from the New World
   (b)   made their home in America
   (c)   were afraid to enter the New World
   (d)   were ancestors of the Clovis people

2 Which of the following words explains why the tools were made of "lightweight material" (line 8)?

(a) effective

(b) distances

(c) lances

(d) portable

3 Discoveries that the archaeologists made tell us that the Clovis people _____.

(a) ate animals

(b) understood animals very well

(c) lived near the animals

(d) pointed sharp tools at the animals

4 Why did the Clovis people hunt huge mammals?

(a) The skeletons of the mammals were valuable to them.

(b) They were afraid of them.

(c) They wanted to get rid of them.

(d) Their meat could feed the people for a week.

5 The writer considers the Clovis people botanists because they _____.

(a) could make baskets out of the plants

(b) were experts at growing plants

(c) could identify the different uses of plants

(d) liked to find out about plants

Glossary

competent (line 10): to have the ability, knowledge and skill to do something very well

A competent pilot will know what to do when he meets with bad weather conditions while in the air.

sustenance (line 13): food that is needed by people, plants and animals to stay alive

The tribal groups get their sustenance mainly from the forest.

restricted (line 17): limited

Membership in this club is restricted to those above twenty-one years old.

ailment (line 20): illness

My grandmother often grumbles about her ailments when we visit her.

 **EXERCISE 22**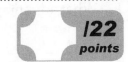

Read the passage carefully.

Jean Pierre was an artist in France. Having been trained in art at a young age, he was given a head start in the industry. By the time he started his career, he was already well-known among those in the industry and avid art collectors.

5   At the tender age of eight, Jean's father sent him to a famous art school. Disillusioned with the way Jean was performing in a regular school, his father had decided that the next best thing was to give him a strong foundation in art. He wanted to be sure that Jean would be able to earn a living when he could no longer provide for him.

10   While sketching a picture in class one day, Jean came across a painting of a famous artist. He was so impressed by it that he wanted to find out more about it. He finally realized where his talent lay. Abstract art was what interested him. Jean did away with the conventional lines and curves that he always used for his drawings and began expressing himself in another
15   way. It was not easy to understand what Jean was painting but many people were attracted to the way he mixed colors and the large expressive strokes that he used across the canvas.

Today, Jean's work is in demand everywhere. His paintings hang in museums and he has even started his own art class, teaching would-be artists
20   the techniques of abstract art.

Answer the following questions in complete sentences citing evidence from the text.

1 What advantage did Jean have when he first started out in the industry?

_____

_____

2 Why was Jean able to get a head start in the industry?

_____

_____

3 What do you think Jean's performance was like in the non-art school?

_____

_____

4 How do you know that Jean's father realized how important art was?

_____

_____

5 Why was Jean's father concerned about his performance in school?

_____

_____

6 What type of art do you think the "famous artist" (line 11) drew?

_____

_____

7 What technique did Jean probably use when he first joined the art class?

_____

_____

8 What type of art can a person do with conventional lines and curves?

_____

_____

9 What do you think made Jean's paintings stand out?

_____

_____

10 Name two ways Jean has helped people to find out more about abstract art.

_____

_____

11 What is the main idea of the text? How does the author develop this idea? Use examples from the text to support your analysis.

_____

_____

_____

Glossary

head start (line 2): an advantage over other people
Attaining good results in school will give you a head start when looking for a job.

avid (line 3): to be very interested in something
Janet is an avid reader who can read ten storybooks a week.

disillusioned (line 6): to be disappointed by something that you thought was good
I was disillusioned when I entered the theme park and found out that there was no roller coaster.

foundation (line 7): basic and most important areas in something
You must have a strong foundation in music before you can write your own songs.

conventional (line 13): a practice or belief that is accepted as normal by most people because it has been around for a long time
Running and shouting at a playground is conventional behavior for children.

technique (line 20): a method of doing something
It is not easy to learn the techniques of writing a good story.

MCQ
ADVANCED

EXERCISE 23

/5
points

Read the information report carefully.

Charity organizations are responsible for most of the help extended to the destitute. Each organization caters to a different group of people.

The Red Cross is a well-known organization that has centers in countries all over the world. It had its beginnings in a small Italian town in 1859. A
5 fierce battle was taking place then and more than forty thousand people were wounded. The medical services of the army were inadequate. The situation horrified a Swiss businessman who then wrote a book depicting the dreadful situation. His book was the impetus for the setting up of charity organizations.

10 Today, countries emulate the workings of the Red Cross. They carry out fund raising activities to help children who cannot receive an education or victims of natural disasters. Both the young and old contribute willingly to these organizations. In fact, without these charity organizations, millions of people around the world would perish because of poverty or natural
15 disasters.

In India, a compassionate woman started PUSS (Palli Unnayan Sevi Samiti). Supported by social workers and teachers, she has helped hundreds of children receive a proper education. Without her help, the literacy rate in India would be much lower than what it is today.

20 Charity organizations are crucial today. They cannot function without the benevolent people who help to run these organizations.

Choose the correct answer and fill in the correct letter in parentheses.

1 The first center of the Red Cross was in _____.
    (a) India   (c) Sweden
    (b) Italy   (d) Switzerland

2 The Red Cross was first set up to help _____.
- (a) injured soldiers
- (b) sick children
- (c) children with no education
- (d) victims of natural disasters

3 What was the "book" (line 7) about?
- (a) Sick children
- (b) How the rich can help the poor
- (c) People suffering in a war
- (d) Different charity organizations

4 Charity organizations obtain their funds through _____.
- (a) donations
- (b) victims
- (c) the government
- (d) the Red Cross

5 According to the passage, India is facing the problem of _____.
- (a) natural disasters
- (b) poor and hungry children
- (c) children with no homes
- (d) large numbers of uneducated children

Glossary

destitute (line 2): having no money, food or possessions
The old lady was left a destitute when her children took all her money.

impetus (line 8): an influence that causes something to happen quickly
The evidence of corruption provides further impetus for the change in government.

emulate (line 10): to imitate someone because you admire him very much
Tom dresses like his father and emulates the way he behaves.

perish (line 14): to die
Many people perished when the building exploded.

benevolent (line 21): kind and helpful
A benevolent man adopted the homeless girl.

EXERCISE 24

Read the passage carefully.

The burglars entered the museum near closing time. Both tourists and locals thronged the place at this time. The burglars wore grey suits like most of the visitors. The guards waved them through.

They entered the first hall. A huge picture of the Mona Lisa dangled from
5   the ceiling. Her radiance lighted up the room which was filled with much smaller yet similarly muted colored paintings. Her eyes seemed to gaze at every visitor in a way that the other paintings could not.

At the end of the hall, the third person dropped her briefcase onto the floor and lifted a painting slightly. She pressed the tiny button and waited for
10   a few seconds, holding her breath. Who would have thought that it would be so simple to deactivate the alarm system? She lifted the painting from its place just as an alarm in the next hall sounded. The museum became dark and smoky and there was a commotion outside the hall. The lady smirked. Robert had done a good job up in the control room. Sliding the picture into
15   her briefcase, she ran out before a barrier descended. She saw her friends in the distance just as she stepped out of the museum. On her right, a man in overalls entered an inconspicuous white van before driving off into the sunset.

Answer the following questions in complete sentences citing evidence from the text.

(1) Who allowed the burglars to enter the museum?

_____

_____

2 Why were the burglars able to get into the museum unnoticed?

_____

_____

3 What do you think attracted a person's attention when he entered the hall?

_____

_____

4 Name two ways in which the Mona Lisa looked different from the other paintings.

_____

_____

5 What do you think was probably in the booklets?

_____

_____

6 Why did the third person carry a briefcase?

_____

_____

7 Which phrase tells you that the burglar was not totally confident that she would be able to take the painting successfully?

_____

_____

8 What was the purpose of sounding the alarm in the next hall?

_____

_____

9 What do you think could be found in the control room?

_____

_____

10 What do you think the "friends" (line 17) and the "man in overalls" (lines 18-19) did to help the lady?

_____

_____

11 What is the main idea of the text? How does the author develop this idea? Use examples from the text to support your analysis.

_____

_____

radiance (line 5): showing great happiness on your face that makes you look attractive

The radiance of the girl's smile made her stand out at the party.

muted (line 6): colors that are not bright

She wore a muted blue dress for her best friend's wedding.

enraptured (line 7): to be filled with delight and fascination by something

We were enraptured by the beautiful sunset.

smirk (line 13): to smile unpleasantly because you have done something or you know something that others do not know

The girl who had finished all her work smirked when she saw her classmates struggling with theirs.

inconspicuous (line 17): not easily noticed

The boy stood at the corner of the room during the party, trying to look inconspicuous.

EXERCISE 25

Read the passage carefully.

When my mother was a child, she used to live near the Rhine river. In those days, traders navigated easily along the waterway, making their way inland to sell their goods.

In the day, my mother watched in awe at ships carrying an impressive
5   amount of goods along the river. She waved to the traders. Her dream was to marry one of them.

My mother's house was a modest home next to a castle. The fortifications in front of the castle still exist today. They guarded the trade route against piracy. My mother's father was one of the five men who stood watch over
10   the Rhine river.

In those days, my mother stuck close to her mother, learning all the skills that were vital in finding a good husband. My mother was an expert seamstress, chef and caregiver.

However, it was not my mother's skills that helped her to marry my
15   father. She often accompanied her father to work. Once, she met the youngest prince who stayed in the castle. He was smitten by her beauty and her gentle ways.

To escape persecution, my mother and her family left their home. However, the prince's love for my mother never faltered. It was like a fairy
20   tale come true when he left his family to set up home with her.

Choose the correct answer and fill in the correct letter in parentheses.

1   The Rhine river was a place for _____.
   (a)   traders to meet with the king
   (b)   those who lived on boats
   (c)   people who wanted to buy goods
   (d)   traders to get from one place to another

2 The area near the Rhine river was home to _____.
- (a) the traders
- (b) the writer's grandparents
- (c) the five men in the castle
- (d) the writer

3 The writer's mother had the intention to marry a trader because she _____.
- (a) liked to travel
- (b) was impressed by the goods that they sold
- (c) wanted to be a trader as well
- (d) felt that traders were good-looking

4 A woman's role in those days was to _____.
- (a) take care of the family
- (b) guard the house
- (c) earn an income
- (d) spend time with her husband

5 Which of the following gives us an idea of how people tried to avoid persecution?
- (a) The writer's grandparents refused to let her mother see the prince again.
- (b) The prince left the castle to look for the writer's mother.
- (c) The writer's mother and her parents left their home.
- (d) The prince never stopped loving the writer's mother.

Glossary

navigate (line 2): to find a way to travel safely from one place to another
We found it difficult to navigate our way through the hills to the village.

fortifications (line 7): buildings or walls that protect a place during an attack
There are fortifications along the mountains in China.

persecution (line 18): cruel and unfair treatment of people
Many people oppose the persecution of the innocent who have been accused of a crime.

falter (line 19): to lose power and strength
Her confidence in winning the marathon never faltered even though she fell twice during the race.

DATE: .... NAME: ....

CLASS: ....

EXERCISE 26

/22 points

Read the passage carefully.

Chinese and Western operas have existed for a long time but they have always been considered an enigma. Singing, abstract props and elaborate costumes come together to form a wide variety of stories.

5   Operas tell stories that involve a wide variety of feelings. There are tender moments as well as relentless violence in just one opera. Chinese operas often depict soldiers in a battle. Sometimes, even the supernatural like fairies are involved. These stories sometimes exaggerate the cultural beliefs of some Chinese.

Western operas too have stories that involve myths and legends. The
10 "Magic Flute" is connected to the worship of Isis, an ancient Egyptian goddess. The story revolves around a magic flute that has the magical powers to provide assistance in times of peril.

Even without knowledge of the language, it is easy to find out what the opera is about. Face painting is uniform across the cultures. Certain colors
15 are used for the evil characters. Props, although minimal and simple, are effectively used and they are immediately recognized by the audience.

One interesting aspect of operas is the integral role that music plays in them. The actors sing the songs and the audiences listen to find out what the story is about. Chinese operas use mostly stringed and percussion instruments.
20 Western opera makes use of the violin and more instruments like the double bass that provide a mellow sound. Without the music, there will be no opera.

Both operas use music in the same way — to portray a range of feelings to the audience. Soft music is used to show tender loving moments. When
25 the music gradually becomes louder, it is a signal that something is about to happen. Loud music is usually used to show violence or great excitement.

Sadlier School

Answer the following questions in complete sentences citing evidence from the text.

① What are the three things that operas use to tell stories?

_____

_____

② Which word in the passage is opposite in meaning to "elaborate" (line 2)?

_____

_____

③ Why does the writer say that only the beliefs of "some Chinese" (line 8) are exaggerated?

_____

_____

④ Why is the "Magic Flute" considered a myth and legend?

_____

_____

⑤ Why might an opera be understood even among those who do not know the language?

_____

_____

⑥ Why does the writer consider the props effectively used?

_____

_____

7 Why does the writer say that there will be "no opera" without music?

_____

_____

8 What is the difference between the music used in Chinese and Western operas?

_____

_____

9 When does the music in an opera become increasingly louder?

_____

_____

10 Describe the music that is used to show friendly and happy feelings.

_____

_____

11 What is the main idea of the text? How does the author develop this idea? Use examples from the text to support your analysis.

_____

_____

enigma (line 2): someone or something that is difficult to understand
How the robbery could have been carried out despite the tight security remains an enigma to the police.

exaggerate (line 7): to say something that is more than the truth
Simon exaggerated what he saw and did at the beach resort when he told his friends about his holiday.

integral (line 17): an important part of a whole
Having a happy and caring family is integral to the well-being of a child.

percussion (line 19): musical instruments that refer to drums, cymbals and tambourines which you hit to make music
My uncle is in the percussion section of the orchestra.

mellow (line 21): a sound that is very pleasant to listen to
I like to listen to my grandfather's mellow voice as he tells me stories about his childhood.

 **EXERCISE 27**

 **/5**
points

Read the passage carefully.

A day after I celebrated my thirteenth birthday, the Americans dropped the atomic bombs on Hiroshima and Nagasaki. I recall hearing my parents talking to the neighbors in hushed tones. No one was sure of the implications but it was the day when our lives began improving.

5   My siblings and I no longer had to bow to the Japanese soldiers who marched past. I overheard my parents saying that the soldiers were being sent back to Japan.

In the streets, more children were running around and playing. The curfew had been lifted because my brother returned home past midnight one 10   day and no one uttered a word. The ban on buying more than one packet of rice per family was also lifted. For once in many years, there was a little more food during dinnertime.

I was relieved that the war was finally over. However, things were tough. The war had left the country in ruins. The British Administration declared 15   that pre-war Malayan and Straits Settlements currency notes and coins would be made legal tender. The banana notes that had been in circulation during the Japanese Occupation were worthless. Many people were impoverished.

I went back to school although I must admit that I was coerced into it. I had enjoyed the freedom for the past few years. Life was slowly returning 20   to the pre-war days. I was unsure of what it meant but I knew that everyone seemed less perturbed and more cheerful.

Choose the correct answer and fill in the correct letter in parentheses.

1   How old was the writer when the war ended?
    (a)   eleven   (c)   thirteen
    (b)   twelve   (d)   fourteen

The writer probably heard her parents talking to her neighbors about
_____.
    (a)   the effect that the bombs would have on their lives
    (b)   the people who dropped the bombs
    (c)   what they wanted to do once the Japanese left the country
    (d)   the bad times they had been going through

 What restrictions did the people face when the Japanese were in the country?
    (a)   Families could only eat rice and they were not allowed to go out at night.
    (b)   Each family could only purchase one packet of rice and everyone had to be home before midnight.
    (c)   Boys were not allowed to return home after midnight and banana notes could not be used.
    (d)   They were not allowed to leave the house and eat rice.

 After the war, the people found it difficult to _____.
    (a)   leave their homes
    (b)   use the money that they had
    (c)   walk in the streets
    (d)   send their children to school

5 For the writer, life after the war _____.
    (a)   was the same as before
    (b)   was more interesting
    (c)   was simpler than before
    (d)   might not be as good as what others thought it to be

Glossary

implication (line 3): a possible future resulting from a certain situation
What are the implications for the football team if both girls and boys are allowed to play together?

curfew (line 9): a law stating that people must stay indoors after a certain time
A curfew was imposed when the country announced that it was in a state of emergency.

impoverished (line 17): to be made poor
The farmers were impoverished by the drought.

perturbed (line 21): something that makes you worried
The manager was perturbed about his workers rioting against the longer working hours.

OE
ADVANCED

EXERCISE 28

/22
points

Read the passage carefully.

It was dawn when we landed. Jan carried the food and drinks while I lugged the box of medical supplies. Above us the helicopter whirled off. We had finally arrived at the town of Hiras.

Fortunately for us, we met a disaster relief truck along the way. It was
5 a relief to load the heavy supplies in the truck. The man spoke a language we could not comprehend but our purpose was the same. Without him, we would never be able to reach the disaster site sooner.

The truck was driven through rows of thorny bushes before going down a winding dirt road. When the bumpy ride ended, we found ourselves
10 staring at a huge flattened area covered with mud. Jan gasped when she realized that there was possibly life beneath that mud. Groups of people were digging unceasingly. They had already started digging the day before. Modern equipment was not used because there might be some survivors near the surface. No one seemed bothered by the onerous task. Their bodies
15 were filled with grime.

Suddenly someone shouted. It was our first success. We had found a young girl clutching her already dead dog. Her petrified eyes were a contrast to the smiles from everyone. I reached for her. She clasped her hands around my neck and asked for her mother.

20 Jan and I worked for two months. Part of the village was unearthed but only a handful of survivors were found. We were disappointed by how unsuccessful the rescue work had been.

Answer the following questions in complete sentences citing evidence from the text.

1 How did the writer get to Hiras?

_____

_____

2 What supplies were the people in Hiras probably lacking?

_____

_____

3 Why was it lucky for the writer to meet the disaster relief truck?

_____

_____

4 Which phrase explains why the ride was a bumpy one?

_____

_____

5 Why was Jan shocked to know that there could be people below the mud?

_____

_____

6 What do you think made the task of finding survivors very difficult?

_____

_____

7 Write the sentence that tells you that the people had been digging for a long time.

_____

_____

8 How do you think the person who shouted felt?

_____

_____

9 Why was the girl scared?

_____

_____

10 Although part of the village was unearthed, why did the writer think that the rescue work was unsuccessful?

_____

_____

11 What is the main idea of the text? How does the author develop this idea? Use examples from the text to support your analysis.

_____

_____

MCQ
ADVANCED

EXERCISE 29

/5
points

Read the passage carefully.

Children across the street were celebrating the fall of the first snowflake. This was what Nadia longed for but she was not like them. She was not allowed to play in the snow.

Nadia's parents were slaves. They worked for Mr. and Mrs. Flinch who
5   had made it clear that Nadia must not be near their children. She longed to learn to read and write. Every morning, she would hear the children talking excitedly about school. They dressed well unlike Nadia. She had scruffy clothes and unkempt hair. Whenever she tried to neaten herself, her parents would quickly stop her and admonish her. She did not belong to the upper
10 classes.

Nadia heard the key turning in the lock. She jumped up in anticipation of what her parents would have. Their employers were kinder during winter and Nadia would sometimes be lavished with the children's old clothes and food.

15 Nadia saw her parents' faces as they entered. They were beaming with delight. Almost falling out of their hands was a whole turkey! Nadia could not believe her eyes. The turkey would last for days. She would not have to scrimp on the leftovers that she usually had.

The snow could wait. All she wanted to do now was taste the succulent
20 turkey.

Choose the correct answer and fill in the correct letter in parentheses.

1   Nadia wished that she could _____.
   (a)   look at the snow   (c)   talk to the children
   (b)   touch the snow   (d)   play with the children

2 It was easy to tell that Nadia was not in the upper classes because _____.
   - (a) she had long hair
   - (b) she did not know where the school was
   - (c) her clothes were dirty
   - (d) her parents were afraid of Mr. and Mrs. Flinch

3 Nadia wanted to go to school so as to _____.
   - (a) talk to the children
   - (c) meet the teachers
   - (b) be able to get out of the house
   - (d) be literate

4 Nadia "jumped up" (line 11) as she _____.
   - (a) was very hungry
   - (b) needed new clothes for winter
   - (c) wanted to ask her parents if she could go to school
   - (d) knew that her parents would have something for her

5 The first thing that Nadia thought of when she saw what her parents had brought home was _____.
   - (a) how long the turkey would last
   - (b) how kind Mr. and Mrs. Flinch were
   - (c) the type of leftovers she had been eating
   - (d) her parents had not let her down

Glossary

scruffy (line 7): dirty and untidy
I saw a scruffy dog searching for food in the garbage can.

unkempt (line 8): untidy
The garden became unkempt after the owner left for a long holiday.

anticipation (line 11): eagerness about something that is about to happen
The audience waited in anticipation for the concert to start.

lavish (line 13): to give someone or something a lot of presents, money or attention
Mr. and Mrs. Smith lavished a lot of attention on their only child.

scrimp (line 18): to try to spend as little money as possible
The widow scrimps on herself so that she can give her children the best.

succulent (line 19): food that is juicy and delicious
Our mouths watered when we saw the succulent dishes at the buffet.

EXERCISE 30

/22
points

Read the passage carefully.

Skippy and I made our way to the store. Around us, nature was awakening once again. Fruit was waiting to be picked and flowers were in full bloom. I was glad that the cold dreary winter was finally over.

5   We passed a stand selling hot dogs. The tantalizing smell of grilled sausages floated through the air and made my stomach growl. I hurried away from it else I would give in to temptation. I tugged at Skippy's leash and he returned to my side. Around the corner, we met the genial Mr. Reef and his dog, Max. He jeered at Skippy for being on a leash. Skippy retaliated by giving Max one of his fiercest growls. Mr. Reef smiled warmly at us and

10 hurriedly apologized for Max's behavior

When we reached the store, I secured Skippy to a post outside. He whined pitifully as I walked off. In the store, I headed straight for the shelves at the back and reached for the bread that I was supposed to buy for my mother. I picked up a small yellow box on my way to the cashier.

15   Outside, Skippy was up to his usual antics. He must have known. "After lunch," I smiled at him. "Let's go. Mom is waiting. I can almost smell the aroma from the kitchen."

There was a quickness in his step and he pulled at his leash. Laughing, I began running and Skippy scampered along beside me.

Answer the following questions in complete sentences citing evidence from the text.

1 What season had ended?

_____

_____

2 Why did the writer like spring?

_____

_____

3 Which phrase tells you that the writer was probably feeling hungry?

_____

_____

4 Why was Skippy not at the writer's side?

_____

_____

5 Which phrase tells us what "genial" (line 7) is?

_____

_____

6 How do you know that Skippy was angry with Max?

_____

_____

7 Why do you think Skippy whined when the writer left him outside the store?

_____

_____

8 What do you think was the small yellow packet that the writer bought?

_____

_____

9 What were Skippy and the writer going to do when they reached home?

_____

_____

10 What did Skippy do to tell the writer that he wanted to go home earlier?

_____

_____

11 What is the main idea of the text? How does the author develop this idea? Use examples from the text to support your analysis.

_____

_____

Glossary

dreary (line 3): something that is dull so it makes you feel bored or upset
I had a dreary time learning to play chess.

tantalizing (line 4): something that creates hope and desire in you because you want to have it but is probably unlikely to provide the satisfaction you need
Tom gave me a tantalizing smile when I asked him about the surprise he had planned for me.

jeer (line 8): to say rude things to someone to show him that he is not worthy of respect
Everyone jeered at the proud boy when he lost the tennis match.

retaliate (line 8): to do harm to a person because he has done the same thing to you
When the bully punched Thomas, he retaliated by kicking him.

antics (line 15): funny, unusual or annoying behavior
My brother made everyone laugh with his antics.

scamper (line 19): to take small, quick and bouncy steps
The squirrel scampered up the tree.

MCQ
ADVANCED

EXERCISE 31

/5
points

Read the passage carefully.

In 1938, the Wilhelm Gustloff was a passenger cruise ship for the German people. However, this was before war broke out in 1939. The ship became first a barracks for the military and later an escape vessel for thousands of refugees escaping from the Russians.

5　　At the height of the war, the only alternative of escape was by sea. About ten thousand Germans thronged the ship and it left Danzig Bay with two torpedo boats as escorts. However, one of the boats was forced to return to base when water began leaking in.

When the first of three torpedoes was launched, the ship and her
10　passengers had little hope of escape. Although the people rushed to the upper decks to gain access to the lifeboats, they realized that the cables to lower most of the lifeboats were frozen. This made it difficult to launch them. Many jumped overboard but in the freezing cold, they became even more vulnerable.

15　　Masses of innocent lives were lost when the ship sank. Since then, people have wondered if the tragedy could have been averted had the crew been prepared. The lifeboats could have been tested before the voyage began even if it might have caused panic among the passengers. The route could have been better planned and the crew less complacent about their enemy's
20　ability to destroy their ship.

Choose the correct answer and fill in the correct letter in parentheses.

1　The Wilhelm Gustloff was first used _____.
　　(a)　for leisure　　　　　　　　(c)　as a military barracks
　　(b)　as a hospital　　　　　　　(d)　as an escape vessel

2 During the war, many Germans boarded the Wilhelm Gustloff to _____.
  - (a) fight the enemy
  - (b) return to their homes
  - (c) go to a safe place
  - (d) make their home permanently on the ship

3 The torpedoes were launched by _____.
  - (a) the Germans
  - (b) the refugees
  - (c) the captain of the Wilhelm Gustloff
  - (d) the enemies of the Germans

4 The passengers were unable to escape as _____.
  - (a) they were very cold
  - (b) it was nighttime
  - (c) the lifeboats could not be used
  - (d) they did not know how to swim

5 One way the tragedy could have been prevented would be to _____.
  - (a) tell the passengers what might happen
  - (b) take safety precautions before the voyage started
  - (c) travel by land instead of by sea
  - (d) have more experienced crew on board

Glossary

refugee (line 4): a person who is forced to leave his country because of war or the beliefs that he has
The police captured hundreds of Vietnamese refugees who had come to the country illegally.

throng (line 6): to go somewhere in large numbers
Mourners thronged to the funeral of the late President.

vulnerable (line 14): someone who is weak and can be easily hurt
Children are the most vulnerable party whenever parents choose to settle for a divorce.

avert (line 16): to prevent something unpleasant from happening
To avert a fight, John apologized to the bully and walked away quickly.

complacent (line 19): to be very pleased with yourself about something and to feel that there is nothing for you to worry about
The complacent boy was shocked when he did not win the drawing competition.

EXERCISE 32

/22 points

Read the passage carefully.

The sun directly above them beat down relentlessly as they drove through the desert landscape. Magnificent desert boulders sprouted towards the skyline. A solitary man could be seen herding his ships of the deserts.

As the day wore on, the sky started to turn hazy. Nellie joked that there
5 was going to be a heavy downpour. Their laughter subsided when the sky suddenly darkened and a huge brown cloud in the distance advanced towards their vehicle with great speed. As it neared, Nellie could see it swirling uncontrollably, pushed about by the gale. They had never seen such an awesome sight before. Earlier that day, they were told that a desert
10 trip was never complete without experiencing first-hand a sandstorm. They looked all around them, suddenly feeling isolated and insecure. Their vehicle started to shake violently. Thinking quickly, Dean parked the car with its side in the direction of the oncoming wind so that the windscreen would not shatter. By now, they could see nothing but swirling sand. As they sat waiting
15 in the car, they listened to the drone of the storm outside, not knowing how long they would be trapped in the car. The occasional rocking kept them on their toes. They braced themselves in case the car overturned.

After some time, Dean noticed that the floor of their car had mini sand dunes. Somehow, the sand had made its way through the crevices of the door
20 and air vents. Dean kicked at the sand absent-mindedly, not quite knowing what to make out of this. The sandstorm finally showed signs of ceasing after two hours. As the wind calmed, Nellie and Dean got out of their car and inspected it. The metallic blue car they had started out with was now a rusty peach. All the dents, rust and grease had disappeared in the two hours
25 of sandblasting. Dean grabbed his camera and took a picture of the license plate that was barely readable. Then they posed for a picture together with the car in the background.

The sky was clear again. Dean started the engine and they continued their journey towards the east. Soon, they heard the barking of dogs from a

30 Bedouin village.

Answer the following questions in complete sentences citing evidence from the text.

① At what time of the day were Nellie and Dean on the road in the first paragraph?

_____

_____

② What was the man in line 3 doing in the desert?

_____

_____

③ Why was Nellie's comment considered a joke?

_____

_____

④ What were the signs of an onset of a sandstorm?

_____

_____

⑤ Why were Nellie and Dean eager to experience a sandstorm?

_____

_____

6 Why did Dean move the car as the sandstorm approached?

_____

_____

7 In your own words, explain how the couple felt as they waited in the car.

_____

_____

8 How did the sand get into the car?

_____

_____

9 Why was the color of their car different after the sandstorm?

_____

_____

10 Why would Dean and Nellie want a photograph of themselves with the car after the sandstorm?

_____

_____

11 What is the main idea of the text? How does the author develop this idea? Use examples from the text to support your analysis.

_____

_____

Glossary

wore on (line 4): referring to time that is passing slowly
   Jasmine's sore throat grew worse as the day wore on.

on their toes (line 16-17): to be alert for something that might happen
   The hikers were on their toes as they climbed the mountain in case a landslide occurred.

MCQ
ADVANCED

EXERCISE 33

/5
points

Read the passage carefully.

You have heard of dogs being trained to play dead but what about a snake who does just that without you telling it to?

The hognose is cream-colored with several brown blotches running down its body. Compared to the female, the male has more dorsal spots. The
5 hognose has a keen sense of smell and digs into the sand to look for prey, mainly amphibians and other reptiles.

The hognose is famous for its display of self-defence. If it feels threatened by an alien presence, it will put up a "performance" to scare away the potential threat. Remaining in its spot, it rears up with a cobra-like hood, making it
10 look larger than it actually is. Then it strikes out, hissing menacingly, swaying its head back and forth, giving the impression of an impending attack. This sequence of actions usually does the trick and most of its intruders will take to their heels, thinking that it is a poisonous reptile.

If, however, these antics fail to shake off the intruder, the hognose has
15 another card up its sleeves. It rolls over and goes into a convulsion-like state. After a while, it lays motionless with its mouth open and its tongue dangling out. Some hognoses may even bleed in its mouth or expel faeces! If it is on its belly, it will automatically flip over, as if to silently persuade the intruder that it is truly dead. Should the hognose be picked up, it is limp. It will never
20 hurt a person, even if it is provoked. Once the hognose senses that danger is gone, it will lift its head, flip onto its belly and slither away!

Choose the correct answer and fill in the correct letter in parentheses.

1 The spots on the male hognose are found _____ of its body.
  (a) on the underside
  (c) at the sides
  (b) on the back
  (d) only at the front part

2 According to the passage, which of the following animals is not part of a hognose's diet?
    (a)   Lizard   (c)   Toad
    (b)   Hen   (d)   Salamander

3 For the hognose, the first step to holding its ground when threatened is to
_____.
    (a)   move its head to and fro to distract the intruder
    (b)   dangle its tongue out and hiss menacingly
    (c)   dart about as if ready to strike
    (d)   lift itself up to look bigger

4 By shaking its body violently and uncontrollably, the hognose hopes to
_____.
    (a)   bleed in its mouth
    (b)   flip itself over
    (c)   entice the intruder to pick it up so that it can attack him
    (d)   deceive the intruder into thinking that it is going to die

5 "Should the hognose be picked up, ..., even if it is provoked." (lines 19-20)
This tells us that a hognose is _____.
    (a)   patient and cunning
    (b)   tolerant and aloof
    (c)   gentle and docile
    (d)   cunning and ferocious

Glossary

> **blotch** (line 3): a colored mark on the skin
> The pink blotch on her arm is a birthmark.
>
> **dorsal** (line 4): the back of an animal
> I could see the dorsal fin of a shark sticking out of the water.

EXERCISE 34

/22
points

Read the passage carefully.

Mrs. Ray was sipping her afternoon tea when she noticed a boy in the park across from her house. He caught her attention as she seldom saw anyone in the park at this time. He was circling furtively around the park.

When he came closer, she got a better look at him. He looked vaguely
5 familiar. Deciding that it was probably her imagination, she went inside as the late afternoon sun began to set.

During dinner, a passport-sized photograph in the newspapers caught her attention. "The boy!" she exclaimed. Dashing to the window, she craned her neck for a glimpse of the boy. However, the park was deserted.

10 She was about to call the police when she heard a light rap on her door. To her astonishment, the same boy was standing before her eyes. There were wounds on his arms and legs and when she looked closer, she saw that the white shirt with patches of dirt was actually a school uniform.

The feeble boy mumbled something to her before collapsing. He only
15 said a few words and he was barely audible but she heard him. She was in such a daze that she did not know who she was supposed to call. A while later, she finally managed to call the police.

Lionel Frank was the son of a well-known businessman. He had been kidnapped a few days ago and the kidnappers had demanded a hefty sum.
20 Undercover agents were on their way to hand over the ransom when Mrs. Ray made the call. Her timely act had saved the boy's life.

Answer the following questions in complete sentences citing evidence from the text.

(1) How do you know that Mrs. Ray often looked outside the window while having tea?

_____

_____

(2) Which word tells you that the boy probably did not know his way around the park?

_____

_____

(3) How did Mrs. Ray react to the boy when she got a better look at him?

_____

_____

(4) What made Mrs. Ray recognize the boy at the park?

_____

_____

(5) Why was Mrs. Ray astonished?

_____

_____

(6) What evidence is there in the passage to show that the boy was probably in pain?

_____

_____

★★★**100**★★★
Exercise 34

7 Why did Mrs. Ray not notice the boy's uniform at first?

_____

_____

8 How do you know that the boy was feeling weak?

_____

_____

9 What do you think the boy said to Mrs. Ray?

_____

_____

10 What were the police about to do when Mrs. Ray called them?

_____

_____

11 What is the main idea of the text? How does the author develop this idea? Use examples from the text to support your analysis.

_____

_____

Glossary

furtively (line 3): to behave as though you want something to be kept a secret
   The robber looked around furtively before forcing open the gate.

vaguely (line 4): not clearly
   I vaguely remember the teacher telling us that we would be going to the science laboratory today.

crane (line 8): to stretch or lean over so as to see something
   Michael craned forward to see the accident.

audible (line 15): something that is loud enough to be heard
   My breathing was audible in the quiet room.

hefty (line 19): large and heavy
   The hefty man could lift two ladies onto his shoulders.

EXERCISE 35

/5
points

Read the passage carefully.

The jungle was awash in lime green leaves at the entrance but darkened leaves were found on the lower branches. I felt like the leaves. My face basked in the light while my feet were cast in darkness.

In the distance a high-pitched mating call sounded. A bird's prominent
5   yellow and red feathers peeked out from among the leaves just above me. My camera was ready but I was not quick enough. I saw yellow and red flashing past.

I felt disappointed but not dejected. My simple outfit made it easier for me to move around. My pants fell just to my ankles and my brown
10   T-shirt hung loosely on my thin frame. I had all I needed in my pockets and I was not burdened by extra items. I got up and raced quietly to my next spot.

I never expected the one I was looking for to beckon me. It was rare for it to leave the upper branches. I took a few shots. Then, I enticed it to come
15   nearer with the many birdseeds I tossed in front of me. It took the bait and hopped forward. Surprising me once again, it pecked at only one seed before flying off. There was no time to capture the bird in action on film.

The sun was setting and I returned home. I had taken enough photographs to remind myself of the outing.

Choose the correct answer and fill in the correct letter in parentheses.

1   From the description of the jungle, we know that _____ .
   (a)   the whole place was very dark
   (b)   sunlight did not reach the ground
   (c)   there were many dead leaves on the ground
   (d)   the writer could not see where she was going

② How did the writer spot the yellow and red bird?
    (a)   It was calling her.
    (b)   There was a mating call.
    (c)   The bird stood out among the leaves.
    (d)   She saw the bird moving.

③ The writer was probably not dejected because she _____.
    (a)   knew that it would be easy for her to search for another bird
    (b)   knew where to look for more birds
    (c)   had already taken a photograph of the bird
    (d)   did not like the bird

④ The writer's outfit was "simple" (line 8) because it _____.
    (a)   had pockets
    (b)   was loose
    (c)   covered her legs
    (d)   consisted of a T-shirt and a pair of pants

⑤ The writer said that she was surprised "once again" (line 16). What two things made her surprised?
    (a)   A bird called out to her and it only took one of the birdseeds on the ground.
    (b)   She was able to get photographs of the bird and see it eat.
    (c)   The bird did not like birdseeds and it could perch on a twig.
    (d)   The bird perched on her and took the birdseeds.

Glossary

awash (line 1): to be filled with a large amount of something
The small city was awash with high-rise buildings.

dejected (line 8): unhappy, disappointed or sad
Jim was dejected when his classmates did not select him as the monitor.

burdened (line 11): to be holding or carrying something with great difficulty
The campers were burdened with the large numbers of canned food they had in their haversacks.

beckon (line 13): to signal to someone to move towards you
"Come here and look at this fish!" my friend beckoned to me excitedly.

Sadlier School

DATE: .... NAME: ....

CLASS: ....

EXERCISE 36

/22
points

Read the passage carefully.

The sports meet was in progress and the cheering reverberated throughout the stadium. Then silence fell over the place as everyone waited in anticipation. They were eager to watch the most interesting race at the meet.

A whistle blew and eight athletic boys dashed ahead. Undaunted by the
5   blazing sun, a tall thin boy overtook one competitor after another until he was far ahead of everyone else.

At the speed he was running, one would expect some of the spectators to cheer for the other competitors. Their hopes of winning were dashed. They could only hope for second place.

10   Even before Kieran tore through the finishing line, the crowd was on their feet, clapping their congratulations. Kieran did none of what winners usually did. He walked straight to the shelter instead of sprawling on the track. He immediately entered the changing room instead of waving at his supporters.

15   Kieran appeared when the announcement for the winners was made. Standing next to the second and third place winners, his lanky frame was accentuated. Kieran was allowed to speak. "I would like to thank everyone who came down to support me. Everyone has the potential to be like me. Compete with yourself and not with others and you'll see the results."
20   The applause started again. The humble boy looked up and waved at the audience. Once again, he had demonstrated how talented he was. Kieran was certainly the star of the track and field event.

Sadlier School

Answer the following questions in complete sentences citing evidence from the text.

1 Why were the spectators waiting in "anticipation" (line 3)?

_____

_____

2 Which word tells you that Kieran was not ahead of the other competitors throughout the whole race?

_____

_____

3 Why should the spectators be cheering for the other competitors?

_____

_____

4 Why did the crowd congratulate Kieran before he reached the finishing line?

_____

_____

5 What was Kieran expected to do but did not?

_____

_____

6 How did the other prize winners look next to Kieran?

_____

_____

7 How did Kieran show his appreciation for those who supported him?

_____

_____

8 From his speech, how did Kieran show that he was a humble person?

_____

_____

9 In what way did Kieran show that he was "talented" (line 21)?

_____

_____

10 What qualities does a true winner have?

_____

_____

11 What is the main idea of the text? How does the author develop this idea? Use examples from the text to support your analysis.

_____

_____

reverberate (line 1): a loud sound that echoes around
The baby's cries reverberated throughout the house.

undaunted (line 4): not discouraged by difficulties or danger
Undaunted by the cold weather, the mountaineers continued their climb.

dash someone's hopes (line 8): to tell someone that what he wants is not possible
My hope of playing football in the national team was dashed when I suffered a permanent knee injury.

sprawl (line 12): to lie flat on the ground with your legs and arms spread out
My brother was sprawled out on the floor watching television when I came home.

lanky (line 16): tall and thin
The lanky man found it difficult to stand on the crowded bus.

accentuate (line 17): to make something more noticeable
Her round face was accentuated by her short frizzy hair.

DATE: .... NAME: ....

CLASS: ....

/5
points

Read the passage carefully.

Oil spills are common occurrences in the sea. Oil spills that contaminate coastal amenity areas can interfere with recreational activities. Those who make a living from the tourist trade in these areas can be affected as boating, angling, diving and swimming will cease until the oil spill is cleaned up.

5 However, this only has a short-term impact and before long, things are back to normal.

The impact of oil spills on marine life has more severe consequences. When the sea creatures ingest food that is contaminated with oil, the amount of oil consumed is usually not fatal. However, if bigger creatures consume

10 large numbers of these sea creatures, the level of toxicity in their bodies can be high enough to cause their death.

The main concern with oil spills is what it can do to the body of marine life. Crude oil is usually stickier than refined oil and it will stick to the fur or feathers of animals. This can cause hypothermia in birds that make their

15 homes near the water. Animals like penguins can lose the insulation and waterproofing properties of their feathers. Fur seal pups do not have blubber yet and when oil sticks to them, they can also suffer from hypothermia.

When refined oil spills, they also cause massive damage to the environment. If the oil spill occurs near the shore, turtle eggs might be

20 contaminated. Although refined oil is not as sticky as crude oil, it is more poisonous. Much of marine life has been destroyed when refined oil spills into the ocean. Creatures have died after consuming polluted seawater and the roots of mangrove plants have also been affected.

Sadlier School

Choose the correct answer and fill in the correct letter in parentheses.

1. Oil spills that affect coastal amenities are not as severe as those on marine life because _____.
   (a) those involved in recreational activities will not come into contact with the oil
   (b) those living along the coast do not consume marine creatures
   (c) activities will return to normal once the oil spills have been cleaned up
   (d) not all types of oil are toxic

2. When marine creatures take in oil into their bodies, _____.
   (a) they will die immediately
   (b) they will die of suffocation after some time
   (c) other creatures which eat a lot of them will eventually die
   (d) other creatures which come into contact with them will die

3. When penguins suffer from hypothermia, they will probably _____.
   (a) die immediately
   (b) be having a fever
   (c) be unable to move
   (d) have low body temperatures

4. From paragraph 3, _____ will help to keep some animals warm.
   (a) skin
   (b) blubber
   (c) crude oil
   (d) different colored feathers

5. What impact does refined oil have on marine life?
   (a) It causes sea creatures to pollute the water.
   (b) It facilitates the growth of mangrove plants.
   (c) It causes turtles to bury their eggs deeper in the sand.
   (d) It prevents the population of sea creatures from increasing.

Glossary

ingest (line 8): to take food into the body
Marine creatures may ingest anything they can find in the sea.

massive (line 18): very big
Massive crowds are expected at the rock concert.

EXERCISE 38

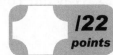

/22
points

Read the passage carefully.

The path was lined with trees so Tom and I tried to walk under them but it was no use. The scorching sun beat down on us. The uphill climb to the peak was an exceptionally difficult one.

I was not about to give up for a substantial amount of preparation had
5   gone into the trip. I had spent hours in the library poring over the climate and geography of the area.

The path ended after a few miles and we walked among sharp-edged saw-grass. Once again, I reassured Tom that the peak was just up ahead. He shook his head in frustration. I had said that many times along the way,
10 thinking that I could placate him. Seeing through my trick, he was about to turn back when we saw the peak up ahead.

With a surge of energy, we raced up the steep slope. At the top, a beautiful sight awaited us. The mountains encircled the peak. Everywhere we turned, we saw the same majestic sight. I felt as though I was in a jade palace as I
15 gazed at the mountain slopes.

Tom and I spent the rest of the morning there before making our way down the abandoned path just after noon. "If this place were lighted, I'm sure it will look beautiful at night," Tom said as he reluctantly left the place.

"We could spend a longer time here too," I added wistfully.

20 We left the place reluctantly and made a promise to return again.

Answer the following questions in complete sentences citing evidence from the text.

1. Why did Tom and the writer walk under the trees?

_____

_____

2. Why was the hike very difficult?

_____

_____

_____

3. Why was the writer unwilling to turn back before she reached the peak?

_____

_____

4. What was the "trick" (line 10) that the writer was referring to?

_____

_____

5. Describe the route to the peak taken by Tom and the writer.

_____

_____

6. What made Tom and the writer travel much faster during the hike?

_____

_____

7 Which sentence gives you an idea of what "encircled" (line 13) means?

_____

_____

8 What do you think the writer saw on the mountain slopes?

_____

_____

9 Why did Tom and the writer have to leave the place in the early afternoon?

_____

_____

10 How do you think Tom and the writer felt about having to leave the place?

_____

_____

11 What is the main idea of the text? How does the author develop this idea? Use examples from the text to support your analysis.

_____

_____

exceptionally (line 3): extremely
Swimming across the English Channel is exceptionally dangerous in cold weather.

substantial (line 4): a large amount
Susie has saved a substantial amount of money after working for ten years.

geography (line 6): the study of places like rivers, mountains, streets and towns and how they are arranged in the countries around the world
We studied the geography of Cambodia before planning our trip there.

placate (line 10): to do or say things to please someone so that he will not feel angry
I tried to placate my brother by promising to buy him a new toy after I spoiled his model airplane.

majestic (line 14): something that is beautiful, large and important
The king looked majestic in his long red robe.

wistful (line 19): a feeling of sadness because you want something that you cannot get
My mother looks wistfully at the diamond rings whenever she passes the jewelry store.

EXERCISE 39

/5
points

Read the passage carefully.

A few days after I started work, I realized that the apron I wore with the golden company emblem was useful for storing apples. I could stuff as many apples as possible and no one would suspect a thing. Sure, the apron sagged with the pockets reaching below my knees but so did the others with
5 sandwiches inside.

By the end of my first week, I followed a routine. I made sure I ate two of the apples for lunch and the rest, I hid in the thermos where I had already drained my coffee. If it was a good day, I would hide the rest of the apples between two thick layers of cloth that I used to drape over my bicycle after
10 I arrived at work.

I spent most of my time at the pier. In the beginning, I did little except observe while the others knocked tirelessly at the wooden and metal planks. There were times when I despised the backbreaking tasks. I was not more than five feet and I weighed one hundred pounds. Yet, once I was familiar
15 with the tasks, I was not exempted from anything. Workers carrying metal planks that were twice their weight were commonplace.

At the end of the first month, I was exuberant. I received my first check. Life was getting better. I was still helping myself to the apples that rolled out from the cartons whenever the movers were transporting them to the ships.

Choose the correct answer and fill in the correct letter in parentheses.

1 The apron was useful for putting apples because it _____.
   (a) had the company emblem
   (b) was also used to keep sandwiches
   (c) would sag below the knees
   (d) had many pockets

2 The "routine" (line 6) that the writer followed referred to _____.
   (a) what he did with his apples
   (b) what he ate for his daily meals
   (c) when he drank his coffee
   (d) how many apples he took every day

3 One task the writer had to do was to _____.
   (a) look for apples that had rolled out from the cartons
   (b) make sure that the other workers were doing their job
   (c) carry cartons of apples to the ships
   (d) carry heavy metal planks

4 Which of the words tells us that strong people were needed to carry out the tasks?
   (a) tirelessly   (c) commonplace
   (b) knocked   (d) backbreaking

5 The writer was very happy with his job because he _____.
   (a) could eat apples
   (b) could learn from the other workers
   (c) could get free apples
   (d) was given more money than what he had hoped for

Glossary

emblem (line 2): a symbol or a design used to represent something such as a club, country or company
The Bald Eagle is the emblem of America.

drape (line 9): to hang a cloth to cover something
A colorful tablecloth was draped over the old wooden table.

exempt (line 15): to be excused from performing something
My mother exempted me from washing the dishes when I was sick.

exuberant (line 17): to be full of energy, excitement and cheerfulness
I was exuberant when I finally saw my father after a month.

DATE: .... NAME: ....

CLASS: ....

EXERCISE *40*

/22
points

Read the journal carefully.

October 6, 1965

Today, Max and Andre asked me if I wanted to go to the pavilion. Of course I did. The Kyrenski dance troupe was here. Oh, how I envy their freedom. Staying with Papa is stifling. I wish I could live on my own like them.

5 October 7, 1965

Max told me all about the performance. It sounded awesome. It lasted for two hours! It must be sheer bliss to be immersed in the music of Mikhail Petrovich and swaying to the rhythm for a whole two hours!

Andre told me that there were openings for new students. I could not believe
10 my ears! It is my dream but I will never be able to fulfill it. Papa is a big obstacle! He keeps telling me that there are no prospects for ballet dancers. But look at the Kyrenski troupe. They are internationally famous. I cannot think of a better way to earn a living.

October 8, 1965

15 I wanted to speak to Papa about taking up dance lessons today. Things looked a little promising. Mama was around and she had promised to help me. However, Papa did not even let me finish my sentence and Mama was so submissive. He told me that I was to be like him and work for the government! He is so old-fashioned. Everyone is pursuing his own interests
20 today. I am not being obstinate.

I am really contemplating leaving the house. Then I will no longer be under his control. I am only worried about Mama. Who will help her with the housework if I leave? She can hardly move without help nowadays.

Answer the following questions in complete sentences citing evidence from the text.

1. Where was the Kyrenski dance troupe performing?

_____

_____

2. What did the writer like to listen to?

_____

_____

3. Where was the "openings for new students" (line 9)?

_____

_____

4. What was the writer's dream?

_____

_____

5. Which phrase in the passage explains what the writer's father meant by "prospects" (line 11)?

_____

_____

6. Why did the writer feel hopeful about being allowed to learn dancing?

_____

_____